PLANT
NUTRITION
Manual

PLANT
NUTRITION
Manual

J. Benton Jones, Jr.

CRC Press
Boca Raton   Boston   London   New York   Washington

Library of Congress Cataloging-in-Publication Data

Catalog record is available from the Library of Congress.

Preface

This manual provides instruction on the basic principles of plant nutrition as they relate to the production of food and fiber plants, as well as for plants whose color and variety appeal to our visual senses.

There are a number of textbooks that describe the complexity of seed germination; how plants grow by utilizing water, carbon dioxide, and 16 elements; and how the plant sets seed. This manual—in a very simple way—describes the principles that determine how plants grow, with emphasis on their nutritional requirements.

Chapter 1 is an introduction to the basic principles of plant nutrition. Chapters 2 and 3 describe the roles of the major elements and micronutrients, respectively. Chapters 4 and 5 describe the techniques that can be used to determine the nutrient-element status of the growing plant by means of plant analyses and tissue tests.

In Appendix D, the nutrient-element requirements for 143 crops are categorized, providing a useful guide for farmers/growers to the probable response to an essential element by plant species. Other appendices contain lists of reference texts, definitions of important terms, and listings of the content and utilization of the major elements by plant species.

This manual has been patterned after the Potash and Phosphate Institute's (PPI) newly revised *International Soil Fertility Manual,* and is designed to complement the PPI manual by extending the material presented into the realm of plant nutrition. Readers will find that these manuals, used together, provide a full picture of the principles of soil fertility and plant nutrition.

About the Author

J. Benton Jones, Jr. is vice president of Micro-Macro International, an analytical laboratory specializing in the assay of soil, plant tissue, water, food, animal feed, and fertilizer. He is also president of his own consulting firm, Benton Laboratories; vice president of a video production company engaged in producing educational videos; and president of a new company, Hydro-Systems, Inc., which manufactures hydroponic growing systems.

Dr. Jones is Professor Emeritus at the University of Georgia. He retired from the university in 1989 after having completed 21 years of service plus 10 years as Professor of Agronomy at the Ohio Agricultural Research and Development Center, Wooster.

He received his B.S. degree from the University of Illinois in 1952 in agricultural science and a M.S. degree in 1956 and a Ph.D. degree in 1959 in agronomy from the Pennsylvania State University.

Dr. Jones is the author of over 200 scientific articles and 15 book chapters, and has written four books. He was editor of two international journals, *Communications in Soil Science and Plant Analysis* for 24 years and the *Journal of Plant Nutrition* for 19 years. Dr. Jones is secretary-treasurer of the Soil and Plant Analysis Council, a scientific society which was founded in 1969, and has been active in the Hydroponic Society of America from its inception, serving on its board of directors for 5 years.

He has traveled extensively with consultancies in the Soviet Union, China, Taiwan, South Korea, Saudi Arabia, Egypt, Costa Rica, Cape Verde, India, Hungary, Kuwait, and Indonesia.

Dr. Jones has received many awards and recognition for his service to the science of soil testing and plant analysis. He is a certified soil and plant scientist under the ARPACS program of the American Society of Agronomy, Fellow of the American Association for the Advancement of Science, Fellow of the American Society of Agronomy, and Fellow of the Soil Science Society of America. An award in his honor, The J. Benton Jones, Jr. Award, established in 1989 by the Soil and Plant Analysis Council, has been given to four international soil scientists, one in each of the years 1991, 1993, 1995, and 1997. Dr. Jones received an Honorary Doctor's Degree from the University of Horticulture, Budapest, Hungary, and is a member of three honorary societies, Sigma Xi, Gamma Sigma Delta, and Phi Kappa Phi. He is listed in *Who's Who in America* as well as a number of other similar biographical listings.

Contents

CHAPTER 1

Plant Nutrition Basics

Functions of Plants

Without green plants—whose leaves contain chlorophyll—our planet would be a very barren place. In the process called *photosynthesis* (Figure 1.1), chlorophyll (Figure 1.2)—when exposed to sunlight (wavelengths between 400 to 700 nm visible light)—is able to convert photon energy into chemical energy (plant carbohydrates). By splitting a water (H_2O) molecule and combining the hydrogen (H^+) proton with carbon dioxide (CO_2), a carbohydrate molecule is formed and a molecule of oxygen (O_2) is released, as is shown in the following equation:

carbon dioxide ($6CO_2$) + water ($6H_2O$)

(in the presence of light and chlorophyll)

carbohydrate ($C_6H_{12}O_6$) + oxygen ($6O_2$)

In the photosynthesis process, there are two biochemical reactions that lead to the production of carbohydrates, one that occurs in C3 plants, the other in C4. Besides a number of important differences between C3 and C4 plants, C3 plants are more sensitive to the carbon dioxide content in the air than C4. The major C3 food plants are wheat, potato, cassava, soybean,

1

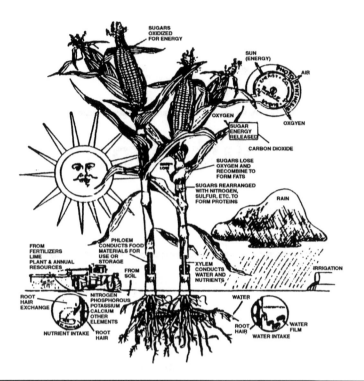

FIGURE 1.1 Photosynthesis illustrated.

oats, and banana, while the common C4 food plants are corn, millet, sorghum, and sugar cane.

In addition to providing food and fiber for man, plant activity also:

- Maintains the balance of atmospheric oxygen and carbon dioxide
- Is a major source for atmospheric moisture through transpiration
- Controls soil erosion
- Recycles soil nutrients
- Is a source of beauty and wonder because of the wide range of growing and flowering habits producing a rainbow of foliage and flower colors

Although there are many thousand different kinds of plants, relatively few species are grown as a source of food for human use. Grain crops, such

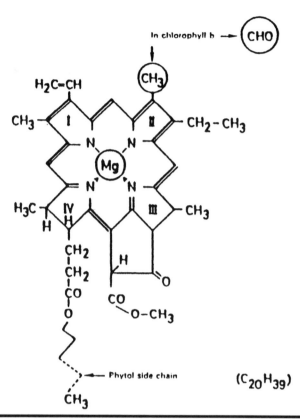

FIGURE 1.2 The chlorophyll molecule.

as corn, wheat, and rice, provide much of the carbohydrate in human diets, while the fruits and vegetables are the major sources of protein and vitamins.

Cotton is the main fiber crop for making cloth, while trees provide the source for building materials, paper, and fuel. Plants are also the source for a number of industrial chemicals and pharmaceuticals.

Plants are far-ranging in their growth habit, cellular complexity, reproduction characteristics, and requirements for growth, such as temperature and moisture tolerance, response to changing light conditions, and nutrient element requirements. Most plants have either a wide or narrow range of adaptability to these environmental conditions.

The nutritional requirements of plants equally vary, a factor that has been effectively manipulated by man to alter yield and quality. In addition, plants have been modified by man to enhance the environment and extend their utilization.

A wide range of plants are used in indoor landscapes to enhance the beauty of buildings and homes, and as turf on athletic fields and golf courses.

Plants are being studied for their adaptation to space enterprises, serving as a means of absorbing carbon dioxide and supplying oxygen, and recycling water and human wastes, as well as providing a potential source of food.

In every one of these uses, plants require specific elements for their normal growth and development, elements that are frequently referred to as *nutrients* or *nutrient elements*. The study of the need and effect of these elements on plant growth and development is called *plant nutrition.*

The Requirements for Essentiality

It was not until the 1800s that scientists began to unravel the mysteries of how green plants grow. A number of theories were put forth to explain plant growth, but through observation and carefully crafted experiments, scientists began to learn what requirements were essential for normal growth and development.

By the beginning of the 1900s, 10 of the now-known 16 essential elements required by plants had been identified.

It might be well to note that the various humus-concept theories of today, which relate to the form that elements exist in the soil and the form that should be provided to plants, had their origins in theories developed by some of these early scientists. The idea that the soil provided "food" for plants or that the humus in the soil was the source of "plant health," still has its proponents today. It has been fairly well established that the *form* of an essential element, whether as an inorganic ion or having its origin derived from an organic matrix, is not a factor that determines the well being of the plant. From a mineral nutrition standpoint, it is the combination of concentration and liable form of an essential element that determines the nutritional status of a plant.

These early scientists had also discovered that the mass of a live plant was essentially composed of water and organic substances, and that in most plants the mineral matter constituted less than 10% and frequently less than 5% of the dry-matter content of the plant. From the analysis of the ash, after the removal of water and the destruction of the organic matter, scientists began to better understand the nutritional requirements of plants, noting which elements were present in the ash and at what concentration. However, at the time there was no system for scientifically establishing the absolute essentiality of elements found in the ash; just their presence was assumed to be related to their essentiality.

In 1939, two plant physiologists at the University of California published their criteria for plant nutrient essentiality, criteria that are still acknowledged today. Arnon and Stout (193a) established three criteria:

- Omission of the element in question must result in abnormal growth, failure to complete the life cycle, or premature death of the plant.
- The element must be specific and not replaceable by another.
- The element must exert its effect directly on growth or metabolism and not some indirect effect such as by antagonizing another element present at a toxic level.

Plant physiologists of today are still attempting to determine if there are additional elements that are essential to plants, applying the three requirements of essentiality as set forth by Arnon and Stout over 50 years ago.

The Essential Elements

By 1890, scientists had already established that carbon (C), hydrogen (H), oxygen (O), nitrogen (N), phosphorus (P), sulfur (S), potassium (K), calcium (Ca), magnesium (Mg), and iron (Fe) were required by plants, and that their absence or low availability resulted in either the death of the plant, or very poor plant growth with accompanying visual symptoms. Between 1922 and 1954, additional elements were determined to be essential: manganese (Mn), copper (Cu), zinc (Zn), molybdenum (Mo), boron (B), and chlorine (Cl). The 16 essential elements, their discoverer, and the discoverer of essentiality are given in Table 1.1.

The concentration required in the plant for normal growth and development varies enormously (the relative range is from 1 to 1 million) among 13 of the essential elements as is shown in Table 1.2. Therefore, it is not surprising that many of the essential elements were not identified until the purification of reagent chemicals was achieved, and the techniques of analytical chemistry had brought detection limits below the milligram level.

The role of the essential elements will be covered in greater detail later in this manual, but a summary is given in Table 1.3.

TABLE 1.1 Discoverer and Discoverer of Essentiality for the Essential Elements

Element	Discoverer	Year	Discoverer of essentiality	Year
C	[a]	[a]	DeSaussure	1804
H	Cavendish	1766	DeSaussure	1804
O	Priestley	1774	DeSaussure	1804
N	Rutherford	1772	DeSaussure	1804
P	Brand	1772	Ville	1860
S	[a]	[a]	von Sachs, Knop	1865
K	Davy	1807	von Sachs, Knop	1860
Ca	Davy	1807	von Sachs, Knop	1860
Mg	Davy	1808	von Sachs, Knop	1860
Fe	[a]	[a]	von Sachs, Knop	
Mn	Scheele	1774	McHargue	1922
Cu	[a]	[a]	Sommer	1931
			Lipman and MacKinnon	1931
Zn	[a]	[a]	Sommer and Lipman	1926
Mo	Hzelm	1782	Arnon and Stout	1939
B	Gay Lussac and Thenard	1808	Sommer and Lipman	1926
Cl	Scheele	1774	Stout	1954

[a] Element known since ancient times.
From Glass, A.D.M. 1989. *Plant Nutrition: An Introduction to Current Concepts.* Jones and Bartlett Publishers, Boston, MA. With permission.

Although it has been almost 40 years since the last of the essential elements, Cl, was identified, there are plant physiologists today actively engaged in determining what additional elements can be added to the current list of 16 (see the section on The Beneficial Elements).

In 1983, Eskew, Welsh, and Cary suggested the establishment of nickel (Ni) as an essential element. There have been additional studies published that would confirm this finding. However, there is no established system for recognizing the essentiality of Ni or other elements that might be added to the current list.

Beneficial Elements

Although no such category has been officially established, many believe that more than the 16 essential elements must be present to ensure the normal growth and development of a plant. In earlier times in the hydroponic culture of plants, an A–Z solution containing 20 elements (Table 1.4)

TABLE 1.2 Average Concentrations of Mineral Nutrients in Plant Dry Matter that Are Sufficient for Adequate Growth

Element	Abbreviation	$\mu mol/g$ dry wt	mg/kg (ppm)	Percent	Relative number of atoms
Molybdenum	Mo	0.001	0.1	—	1
Copper	Cu	0.10	6	—	100
Zinc	Zn	0.30	20	—	300
Manganese	Mn	1.0	50	—	1,000
Iron	Fe	2.0	100	—	2,000
Boron	B	2.0	20	—	2,000
Chlorine	Cl	3.0	100	—	3,000
Sulfur	S	30	—	0.1	30,000
Phosphorus	P	60	—	0.2	60,000
Magnesium	Mg	80	—	0.2	80,000
Calcium	Ca	125	—	0.5	125,000
Potassium	K	250	—	1.0	250,000
Nitrogen	N	1,000	—	1.5	1,000,000

From Epstein, E. 1965. Mineral nutrition, pp. 438–466. In: J. Bonner and J.E. Varner (eds.). *Plant Biochemistry*. Academic Press. Inc., Orlando, FL.

TABLE 1.3 The Essential Elements, Their Form for Uptake, and Functions in the Plant

Essential element	Form for uptake	Functions in the plant
C, H, O, N, S	Ions in solution (HCO_3^-, NO_3^-, NH_4^+, SO_4^{2-}), or gases in the atmosphere (O_2, N_2, SO_2)	Major constituents of organic substances
P, B	Ions in solution (PO_4^{3-}, BO_3^{3-})	Energy transfer reactions and carbohydrate movement
K, Mg, Ca, Cl	Ions in solution (K^+, Mg^{2+}, Ca^{2+}, Cl^-)	Non-specific functions, or specific components of organic compounds, or maintaining ionic balance
Cu, Fe, Mn, Mo, Zn	Ions or chelates in solution (Cu^{2+}, Fe^{2+}, Mn^{2+}, MoO^-, Zn^{2+})	Enable electron transport and catalysts for enzymes

From Mengel, K. and E.A. Kirby. 1987. *Principles of Plant Nutrition*, 4th ed. International Potash Institute, Berne, Switzerland. With permission.

TABLE 1.4   Elements in the A–Z Solution

Element (symbol)	Element (symbol)
Aluminum (Al)	Lithium (Li)
Arsenic (As)	Lead (Pb)
Barium (Ba)	Mercury (Hg)
Bismuth (Bi)	Nickel (Ni)
Bromine (Br)	Rubidium (Rb)
Cadmium (Cd)	Selenium (Se)
Chromium (Cr)	Strontium (Sr)
Cobalt (Co)	Tin (Sn)
Fluorine (F)	Titanium (Ti)
Iodine (I)	Vanadium (V)

was added to the nutrient solution, which contained the known essential elements. The idea was to ensure that almost every element found in the soil would be included in the nutrient solution.

A frequent comparison is made between those elements required by plants with those for animals as illustrated in Table 1.5. There are nine elements, sodium (Na), arsenic (As), chromium (Cr), cobalt (Co), fluorine (F), iodine (I), Ni, selenium (Se), and vanadium (V), required by animals but not yet identified as essential for plants. Of these nine elements, Brown, Welsh, and Cary (1987) have identified Ni as an essential element for plants.

Boron is the only element essential for plants but not so identified for animals (Table 1.5).

There is a considerable difference in how elements are identified as *essential* for animals as compared to plants. Elements that enhance animal growth and function, but will not result in the death of the animal when absent, are classified as essential. If this criterion (growth enhancement) was applied to plants, another class of elements could be established, for indeed there are elements that will enhance plant growth when present compared to plant performance when absent.

There are two kinds of response due to the presence of those elements that have a beneficial effect:

- A direct effect that relates specifically to that element
- Enhancement of growth by means of substitution for an essential element

TABLE 1.5   Essential Elements for Plants and Animals

	Major elements	*Micronutrients*
Plants and animals	Calcium (Ca) Carbon (C) Hydrogen (H) Magnesium (Mg) Nitrogen (N) Oxygen (O) Phosphorus (P) Sulfur (S)	Chlorine (Cl) Copper (Cu) Iron (Fe) Manganese (Mn) Molybdenum (Mo)
Plants only		Boron (B)
Animals only		Arsenic (As) Chromium (Cr) Fluorine (F) Iodine (I) Nickel (Ni) Selenium (Se) Vanadium (V)

An element that fits the first effect is silicon (Si), which enhances the growth and appearance of rice. Without Si being present, rice plants lodge readily and lack stem stiffness. Therefore, for the successful culture of rice, Si must be present in sufficient concentration to ensure high plant performance.

Two other effects of Si are disease resistance—as the presence of Si in the plant is frequently associated with fungus resistance—and enhancement of aluminum (Al) and Fe tolerance by plants. Epstein (1994) has suggested that Si is "essential for some plants; often beneficial."

There have been experiments conducted that suggest that titanium (Ti) can enhance plant growth when supplied in a chelated form that allows Ti to be readily absorbed and utilized by the plant.

An example of the second effect for a beneficial element is Na, which has been found to enhance plant growth and performance for some crops because Na acts as a partial substitute for K. This enhancement/substitution by Na may be species-related, and therefore not applicable to all types of plants. A similar substitution has been suggested for Mo by V.

There is an important indirect requirement for plants that rely primarily on symbiotically-fixed N as the N_2-fixing bacteria have a Co requirement.

Without sufficient Co, the bacteria are not functional, which results in the plant appearing N deficient.

Other Elements in Plants

There are elements other than the 16 essential elements plus those considered beneficial that are also found in plant tissue in a wide range of concentration levels. Various terms have been used to identify these elements, some as heavy metals [because of their high (>50) molecular weight], or by the more general term _trace elements_. The ability to determine these elements, even at very low concentrations (i.e., at parts per billion levels), has come about through the significant advancements made in analytical chemistry over the past several decades. In most instances, very little is known about their effect on plant growth and development. Some of these elements, however, have been found toxic to the plant at elevated concentrations or when in food products and animal feed, which upon entering the food chain can affect the health and well being of animals and humans, respectively. A list of some of these elements and their average ("normal") concentration in plants is given in Table 1.6. Ranges in concentration associated with either sufficiency, normal, toxic, or excessive levels for some of

TABLE 1.6 Trace Element Content of "Reference Plant" (no data from typical accumulator and/or rejector plants)

Trace element	mg/kg	Trace element	mg/kg
Antimony (Sb)	0.1	Iodine (I)	3.0
Arsenic (As)	0.1	Lead (Pb)	1.0
Barium (Ba)	40	Mercury (Hg)	0.1
Beryllium (Be)	0.001	Nickel (Ni)	1.5
Bismuth (Bi)	0.01	Selenium (Se)	0.02
Bromine (Br)	4.0	Silver (Ag)	0.2
Cadmium (Cd)	0.05	Strontium (Sr)	50
Cerium (Ce)	0.5	Thallium (Tl)	0.05
Cesium (Cs)	0.2	Tin (Sn)	0.2
Chromium (Cr)	1.5	Titanium (Ti)	5.0
Fluorine (F)	2.0	Tungsten (W)	0.2
Gallium (Ga)	0.1	Uranium (U)	0.01
Gold (Au)	0.001	Vanadium (V)	0.5

From Markert, B. 1994. In: D.C. Adriano, Z.S. Chen, and S.S. Yang (eds.), _Biogeochemistry of Trace Elements_. Science and Technology Letters. Northwood, New York. With permisssion.

**TABLE 1.7 Normal Range and Suggested Maximum Trace Element
Concentrations for Plant Leaves and Suggested Levels for Corn Leaves**

| | Concentration of metals in plants (mg/kg, dry wt.) | | | |
| | Plant leaves | | Corn leaves | |
Element	Range	Maximum	Range	Maximum
Arsenic (As)	0.01–1.0	2	same	same
Barium (Ba)	10–100	200	same	same
Cadmium (Cd)	0.05–0.20	3	0.05–0.20	1–3[a]
Chromium (Cr)	0.1–0.5	2	0.05–1.0	5
Cobalt (Co)	0.01–0.30	5	same	same
Fluorine (F)	1–5	10	1–10	50
Iodine (I)	0.1–0.5	1	same	same
Lead (Pb)	0.1–5.0	10	same	same
Lithium (Li)	0.2–1.0	5	same	same
Mercury (Hg)	0.001–0.01	0.04	——unknown[b]——	
Nickel (Ni)	0.1–1.0	3	0.1–10	20
Selenium (Se)	0.05–2.0	3	0.1–5	10
Vanadium (V)	0.1–1.0	2	same	same

[a] The level in silage corn must be maintained at a lower level of Cd than for corn grain.
[b] Without more experience, the values of Melsted could be used, but organic complexes of Hg
could provide a threat to animal health at very low levels of total Hg.
From Melsted, S.W. 1973. Soil-plant relationships (some practical considerations in waste management). In: *Proceedings Joint Conference on Recycling Municipal Sludges and Effluents on Land.* University of Illinois, Urbana.

these elements are shown in Tables 1.7–1.9, and the general effects of several of these trace elements on plant growth are listed in Table 1.10.

Some plants are accumulators of a particular trace element, while others have the ability to exclude such elements. Some of these elements are naturally occurring in the environment, others have been added to the environment by human activity.

With the ease of analytical determination available today, efforts are being made by plant scientists to determine more about the plant chemistry of these elements. However, from a practical standpoint today, the presence and/or concentration of many of these elements in plants has little significance in terms of plant production and quality. No doubt this will change as more research is devoted to learning about these elements.

TABLE 1.8   Total Concentrations of Various Elements Typically Found in Plants

| Element | Concentration of metals in plants (mg/kg, dry wt.) | |
	Normal	Toxic
Arsenic (As)	0.1–5	2
Cadmium (Cd)	0.2–0.8	>2
Chromium (Cr)	0.2–1	—
Cobalt (Co)	0.05–0.50	—
Lead (Pb)	0.1–10	—
Nickel (Ni)	1	50
Selenium (Se)	0.02–2.0	50–100
Vanadium (V)	0.1–10	>10

From Pais, I. and J.B. Jones, Jr. 1996. *The Handbook of Trace Elements.* St. Lucie Press, Boca Raton, FL.

Elemental Toxicity

There are a number of elements that can be toxic to plants when present in the rooting medium at elevated concentrations. For example, if in high concentration in the soil solution, most of the micronutrients (B, Cl, Cu, Mn, and Zn) can be toxic to plants.

The toxicity effect may be direct, i.e., the element itself directly impacts the plant, or the effect may be indirect by reducing the availability of another element or by interfering with a normal physiological process within the plant.

An example of a direct toxic-effect element is B, which can significantly reduce the growth of a crop, such as corn, when applied at rates that would be required for a high B-requirement crop, such as peanut or cotton. The carryover of Cu from the long-term use of Cu-based fungicides in orchards and vineyards poses significant problems for subsequent crops. Another direct toxic-effect element is the micronutrient Mn, which can be elevated to toxic concentrations in the soil solution when the pH of a mineral soil is very acid (less than pH 5.5).

An example of an indirect effect element is the micronutrient Zn. If present at high concentrations in the soil solution and/or plant, Zn will interfere with the normal Fe metabolism in the plant, resulting in the development of typical Fe-deficiency symptoms.

TABLE 1.9. Approximate Concentrations of Trace Elements in Mature Leaf Tissue Generalized for Various Species

	Concentration in plants (mg/kg, dry wt.)		
Element	Deficient or normal	Sufficient or toxic	Excessive
Antimony (Sb)	—	7–50	150
Arsenic (As)	—	1–1.7	15–20
Barium (Ba)	—	—	500
Cadmium (Cd)	—	0.05–0.20	5–30
Chromium (Cr)	—	0.1–0.5	5–30
Cobalt (Co)	—	0.02–1	15–50
Fluorine (F)	—	5–30	50–500
Lead (Pb)	—	5–10	30–300
Lithium (Li)	—	3	5–50
Mercury (Hg)	—	—	1–3
Nickel (Ni)	—	0.5–5	10–100
Selenium (Se)	—	0.001–2	5–30
Thallium (Tl)	—	—	20
Tin (Sn)	—	—	60
Titanium (Ti)	0.2–0.5	0.5–2.0	50–200
Vanadium (V)	—	0.2–1.5	5–10
Zirconium (Zr)	0.2–0.5	0.5–2.0	15

From Kabata-Pendias, A. and H. Pendias. 1994. *Trace Elements in Soils and Plants,* 2nd ed., CRC Press, Boca Raton, FL. With permission.

Another essential micronutrient that can indirectly affect plant growth is Cl, which normally exists in the soil solution as the chloride (Cl⁻) ion. The chloride effect is usually due to the presence of salt (NaCl) at concentrations that restrict water and nutrient uptake by plant roots. *Salinity* is a major problem in many areas of the world, the result of the continued use of high salt-containing irrigation water.

The most common non-essential element that is toxic to plants is Al, which can reach toxic levels in the soil solution due to soil acidity. The toxic plant symptoms can take various forms. Frequently plants are stunted, root development is impaired, and plants may appear as P-deficient since Al interferes with the uptake of P by the roots. A list of plant species susceptible and tolerant to Al are given in Table 1.11.

It should be remembered that many elemental toxicities on cropland soils are frequently man-made problems associated with past and present

TABLE 1.10   General Effect of Trace Element Toxicity on Common Cultivars

Element	Symptoms	Sensitive crops
Aluminum (Al)	Overall stunting, dark green leaves, purpling of stems, death of leaf tips, and corolloid and damaged root system	Cereals
Arsenic (As)	Red-brown necrotic spots on old leaves, yellowing or browning of roots, depressed tillering	—
Cadmium (Cd)	Brown margin of leaves, chlorosis, reddish veins and curled leaves, and brown stunted roots	Legumes (bean, soybean), spinach
Chromium (Cr)	Chlorosis of new leaves, injured root growth	—
Cobalt (Co)	Interveinal chlorosis in new leaves, followed by induced Fe chlorosis and white leaf margins and tips, and damaged root tips	—
Fluorine (F)	Margin and leaf tip necrosis, and chlorotic and red-brown points of leaves	Gladiolus, grapes, fruit, trees, and pine trees
Lead (Pb)	Dark green leaves, wilting of older leaves, stunted foliage, and brown short roots	—
Mercury (Hg)	Severe stunting of seedlings and roots, leaf chlorosis and browning of leaf points	Sugar beets, maize, and roses
Nickel (Ni)	Interveinal chlorosis in new leaves, stunted foliage, and brown short roots	Cereals
Rubidium (Rb)	Dark green leaves, stunted foliage, and increasing amount of shoots	—
Selenium (Se)	Interveinal chlorosis or black spots at Se content at about 4 ppm, and complete bleaching or yellowing of younger leaves at higher Se content, pinkish spots on roots	—

From Kabata-Pendias, A. and H. Peddias. 1994. *Trace Elements in Soils and Plants,* 2nd ed., CRC Press, Boca Raton, FL. With permission.

activities, such as the long-term use of chemicals containing a potentially toxic element, increasing soil acidity (lack of adequate and timely liming), and soil disposal of industrial, human (sewage sludge), and animal waste products applied at rates beyond the metal-load capacity of the soil.

Plants themselves have the ability to adjust to metal–element excesses. Some of the possible mechanisms involved in tolerance are:

- Selective uptake of ions
- Decreased permeability of membranes or other differences in the structure and function of membranes
- Immobilization of ions in roots, foliage, and seeds
- Removal of ions from metabolism by deposition (storage) in fixed and/or insoluble forms in various organs and organelles
- Alterations in metabolic patterns—increased enzyme system that is inhibited, or increased antagonistic metabolite, or reduced metabolic pathway by passing an inhibited site
- Adaptation to toxic metal replacement of a physiological metal in an enzyme
- Release of ions from plants by leaching from foliage, guttation, leaf shedding, and excretion from roots

In addition, there are metal element toxicity correlation factors that can affect the sensitivity of plants to a particular element:

- Electronegativity of divalent metals
- Solubility products of sulfides
- Stability of chelates
- Bioavailability

Toxicity and tolerance to the metal element by plants can occur due to elemental interactions, mainly with the major elements (primarily Ca and P, including both antagonistic or synergistic effects. It has been suggested by some that one of the major roles of Ca in the plant is to counter the toxicity effect of the heavy metals.

TABLE 1.11   Crop Susceptibility to Aluminum Toxicity

Very susceptible	Susceptible	Resistant
Alfalfa, barley, beets, lettuce, mustard, timothy	Buckwheat, bush bean, cabbage, hemp, oat, pea, radish, rye, sorghum	Corn, cucumber, redtop, rice, squash, turnip

Concepts of Elemental Availability and Movement

Other than C, H, and O, the remaining essential elements are primarily taken up through the roots as ions that exist in the soil solution.

The one major exception is N, as leguminous plants can also obtain N by means of symbiotic-N_2 fixation. Nitrogen-fixing bacteria invade the plant root of legumes and form a colony that takes shape as a nodule on the root (Figure 1.3). These bacteria receive their energy as carbohydrates from the plant, and they in turn fix atmospheric N_2 into usable N for the plant. Depending on the strain of bacteria, the number of nodules formed, and the aerobic status of the soil surface horizon, sufficient N can be fixed to satisfy the N requirement of the plant. However, the presence of nodules on the roots is not sufficient evidence of nodule activity and performance as the ability of the nodule bacteria to fix atmospheric nitrogen (N_2) is dependent on:

- The fertility level of the soil and nutritional status of the plant
- The status of available mineral N in the soil solution
- The strain of bacteria

As was mentioned earlier, Co is required by the N_2-fixing bacteria to function normally. The efficiency of N_2 fixation is enhanced by a sound soil and plant nutritional status, which ensures a normal healthy growing plant.

If readily available N is present in the soil solution, the efficiency of fixation is reduced. If the available N supply is high, or a significant quantity of fertilizer N has been applied, nodule formation will be significantly impaired.

The ionic form of the essential elements normally found in the soil solution are listed in Table 1.12. Note that various valence states or forms may exist for some of these elements. For example, N can exist as either the ammonium (NH_4^+) cation or nitrate (NO_3^-) anion. Phosphorus will exist as either the dihydrogen phosphate ($H_2PO_4^-$) or monohydrogen phosphate (HPO_4^{2-}) anion, depending on the pH of the soil.

The major cations, calcium (Ca^{2+}), magnesium (Mg^{2+}), and potassium (K^+), are primarily found on the colloidal (clay and humus) exchange complex of the soil, ions that are in equilibrium with that found in the soil solution.

FIGURE 1.3 Nitrogen-fixing nodules on plant roots.

Elements can exist in the soil in either inorganic or organic forms or both. Organic debris, plant residues, and microorganisms are the major sources for B, N, P, and S. As plant and microorganism residues decay, ions of these elements are released into the soil solution. The rate and extent of decomposition that results in their release are dependent on soil temperature, moisture, and degree of aeration.

It should be remembered that the soil and the soil solution are components in an ever-changing complex of dynamic chemical and biological systems, which are affected by temperature, moisture content, pH, level of elements present (whether essential, beneficial, or toxic), and degree of aeration. An element, in its ionic form (see Table 1.12), must be in the soil solution in order to be taken up by plant roots. How these ions are brought into proximity to the roots has been categorized by three processes:

- Mass flow
- Diffusion
- Root interception

These three methods of ion movement and interception are illustrated in Figure 1.4.

As water moves in the soil, the dissolved ions are carried along with the moving water; this process is identified as *mass flow*. For example, the ions of Ca and N [as the nitrate (NO_3^-) anion] are primarily moved in the soil by mass flow. These ions can be carried considerable distances by this process. If the soil moisture content is low, movement by mass flow will be impaired.

Diffusion is the process by which ions move within the soil solution from an area of high concentration to an area of low concentration. Most of the ions of the essential elements are moved by diffusion in the soil solution surrounding plant roots. As ions are absorbed from the soil solution at the root interface, a concentration gradient is formed that moves ions

TABLE 1.12   The Essential Elements and Their Form in the Soil Solution

Element	Symbol	Ionic form
Cations		
Ammonium	NH_4	NH_4^+
Calcium	Ca	Ca^{2+}
Copper	Cu	Cu^{2+}
Iron	Fe	Fe^{2+}, Fe^{3+}
Magnesium	Mg	Mg^{2+}
Manganese	Mn	Mn^{2+}, Mn^{4+}
Potassium	K	K^+
Zinc	Zn	Zn^{2+}
Anions		
Boron	B	BO_3^{3-}
Chloride	Cl	Cl^-
Molybdenum	Mo	MoO^-
Nitrate	NO_3	NO_3^-
Phosphorus	P	$H_2PO_4^-$, HPO_4^{2-}
Sulfur	S	SO_4^{2-}

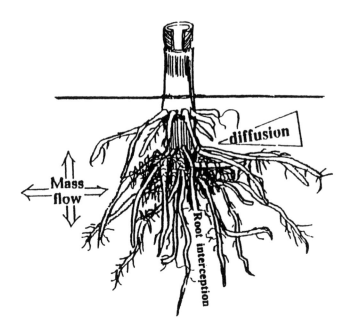

FIGURE 1.4 The elements dissolved in the soil water are carried through the soil by mass flow, and elements within the soil solution move from areas of high to low concentration by diffusion. The plant increases its contact with the soil mass by root interception.

from areas of high concentration to this lower concentration area at the root interface. Movement by this process is measured in a few millimeters. A very low soil moisture status will affect diffusion.

As the plant root system expands, it makes an ever-increasing contact with soil particles and their surrounding solution by the process of *root interception*. Depending on the plant and the conditions in the soil surrounding the growing root tip, root hairs may form, which brings a large surface area for ion absorption into contact with the soil.

Root hair formation, however, tends to be enhanced by conditions of low moisture and nutrient availability. For example, relatively high levels of available N and P surrounding the root reduce the incidence of root hair formation, although the number of fine roots may be enhanced. It is not uncommon to find a large mass of fine roots in or alongside fertilizer bands, for example.

It should be remembered that even with an extensive plant root system, very little of the total soil mass is ever in immediate contact with plant roots. Therefore, the importance of mass flow and diffusion on ion movement combined with *root-soil contact*, all necessary functioning processes that will ensure nutrient element sufficiency for the growing plant. If any of these processes are impaired, nutrient element deficiencies are likely to occur.

Elemental Uptake by Roots

The passage of ions from the soil solution into the plant root is a complex process that is not completely understood. The two phenomena that must be explained are:

- The ability of ions to move against a concentration gradient
- The observed ability of plant roots to selectively absorb or exclude ions

There is also another factor: some plant genotypes have a different ion-selective ability than do other genotypes. An example is the difference in elemental make-up between legumes and grasses. Legumes will have a higher content of Ca and Mg than K; the opposite is true for grasses (higher K in the plant than either Ca or Mg). Some plants are well adapted to specific soil conditions, such as soil salinity, as they are able to cope with the high concentrations of salt [sodium chloride (NaCl)] in the soil solution.

Another notable difference is the ability of some genotypes to more easily absorb Fe from the soil solution (as well as other elements) than other genotypes. This ability to absorb Fe, for example, has led to the classification of some genotypes as *Fe-efficient,* while others are designated *Fe-inefficient.* Iron-efficient genotypes are able to either acidify the rhizosphere, the thin cylinder of root surface and contacting soil, and/or release Fe-fixing or -chelating substances, such as siderophores, which are the most commonly released substances.

Genotype differences are being used in breeding programs to select on the basis of tolerance to certain soil conditions (such as soil salinity) and to remove from the gene pool undesirable traits, such as sensitivity to a particular element or suite of elements, or to reduce the affinity for elements that might be toxic or make the plant unsuitable for use as feed for animals or food for human consumption.

The ability of ions to move across a concentration gradient is associated with plant root respiration; the energy required is generated by root respiration. In order for respiration to occur, oxygen (O_2) is required. Therefore, roots that are not in an aerobic environment will not be able to actively absorb ions.

In addition, ions may passively move from the soil solution into the *free space* that exists in the root, space that represents about 10% of the total internal root volume; which ions or other substances found in the soil solution that will passively move into this free space is dependent on either their ionic or molecular size as the cellular material surrounding the free space has a network of specifically sized pores. Pores act as a filter by keeping certain-sized substances from entering the root.

Roots also exhibit a cation exchange capacity and cations can be added or removed from roots by a demonstrated exchange process. This apparent cation exchange capacity may be one of the factors that gives rise to the ability of certain cations to be taken up by the plant to the exclusion of others.

Ions—which carry an electrical charge—may be excluded from uptake as compared to uncharged molecules, e.g., as the external pH increases, the uptake of B is affected as the ratio of B as boric acid (uncharged molecule) to the borate anion changes. Uptake of P is also influenced by pH as the form of P in the soil solution changes from $H_2PO_4^-$ to HPO_4^{2-} to PO_4^{3-} as the pH increases, giving rise to a change in both size and charge of the anion. By contrast, pH change has no effect on the sulfate (SO_4^{2-}) anion; therefore its uptake is fairly constant with changing pH.

The effect of pH, presence of other cations and anions, and the respiration characteristics of the root play major roles in ion uptake. In general

- pH has a greater impact on cation than anion uptake.
- There is a greater competitiveness among the cations than anions for uptake.
- There is a charge compensation associated with the differential uptake of cations.

Also, there appears to be a *feed-back* system in the root that can regulate the uptake rate of ions.

Root Characteristics

The physical characteristics of the root itself have an influence on ion uptake because as the root changes anatomically, the function and rate of ion uptake is affected. In general, as the distance from the root tip increases, the rate of ion uptake decreases. In addition, at a short distance from the root tip, root hairs may form that will significantly enhance ion uptake due to the large increase in root surface area generated. Root hair development is influenced by the physical and chemical characteristics around the developing root. In addition, the formation of lateral roots will also increase the soil-root contact surface, and in turn, enhance ion uptake.

Carrier and Ion Pump Systems

It is generally believed that a carrier system exists that literally *carries* an ion across the cell membrane, although the specific identification of such carriers has not been determined. An ion is attached to a carrier, then the combined unit is transported from the outer root surface into the root itself. The ion is deposited inside the root with the carrier moving back across the cell membrane to repeat the process with another ion. Another concept is that there exists an ion pump system that assists in the transport of ions across the cell membrane. In order for both of these systems to work, energy is required, which is derived from root respiration.

The Rhizosphere

The rhizosphere is the thin cylinder of soil that immediately surrounds the root. Its pH and other characteristics are considerably different from that of the whole soil. Normally, the pH of the rhizosphere will be more than one unit less than the soil as a whole, the result of released H ions from the respiration process. There is considerable biological activity in the rhizosphere as carbonaceous materials are released or sloughed off from the extending and/or expanding root as it moves through and into the soil, providing readily usable food for bacteria and fungi. These factors significantly influence the availability and uptake of ions from the soil solution into the root. This is one of the reasons why plants can survive on relatively poor soils, i.e., soils whose pH and level of available essential elements may be less than ideal.

Plant roots, their function, and extent of soil contact will significantly influence the growth and development of the whole plant. Any impairment of root function will be evident as a change in the overall physical appearance of the aerial portions of the plant. Nutrient-element insufficiencies can occur even though the overall soil fertility level is adequate to meet the plant requirement due to:

- Roots being impaired or damaged by physical circumstances (compacted soils, anaerobic conditions due to soil crusting, mechanical root pruning, etc.)
- Low soil temperature
- Low soil moisture which impairs ion movement in the soil by either mass flow or diffusion
- Excessive soil water level, which creates an aerobic condition
- Adverse biological activity, such as disease and nematode infestations

Element Translocation within the Plant

Root uptake of an ion does not mean that the absorbed ion will be the automatically translocated into the other portions of the plant. As with the root, there exists a mechanism of transport that carries ions across cell membranes and on into the vascular system, which is about as complex as that required for ions to enter the root.

In general, long-distance upward movement of ions from the root to the growing point is through the xylem, a vessel transport system that carries both water and ions. The downward movement in plants occurs in the phloem, which takes place in living cells. The driving force that moves water, ions, and other dissolved solutes in this complex vascular system comes from a number of sources:

- The transpiration of water from the leaf surfaces of the plant, which draws water from the rooting medium into the root and then up the entire plant
- Root pressure exerted from the roots themselves, pushing water and ions up the plant
- The source-sink phenomenon, which draws water, ions, and solutes from inactive to active expanding portions (growing points, developing fruit, grain, etc.) of the plant

The movement of ions, molecules, and solutes in the xylem is determined to a considerable degree by the transpiration rate, which in turn has an effect on the distribution of these substances into the stems, petioles, leaves, and fruit. In addition, the movement of these various substances is not uniform in terms of rate and type. For example, transpiration enhances the uptake and translocation of uncharged molecules to a greater extent than that of ions.

Both Si and B have been extensively studied, relating transpiration rate with the distribution of these two elements in various plant parts—the higher the transpiration rate by a particular plant part, the higher the concentration of that element in that plant part. It has been found, for example, that the transpiration rate has a considerable effect on the movement of Ca, a lesser effect on Mg, and little influence on K into developing fruit.

Solute and ion movement is unidirectional in the xylem, but bidirectional in the phloem— from source to sink. There is also some cross-transfer from the xylem into the phloem, but not from the phloem into the xylem. The transport rate in the xylem may range from 10 to 100 cm/hour, while that in the phloem is considerably less.

There is also a retranslocation of elements from the shoot to the roots, which has a regulating effect on the uptake rate through the roots. For example, about 20% of the root-shoot transport is taken up by K, related in part to its role as a counterion for nitrate (NO_3) transport in the xylem, a requirement needed for maintenance of cation-anion balance.

As can be seen from this discussion, the movement of ions, molecules, solutes, and water occurs within a fairly complex system of vessels and cells, movement that is driven by both external and internal factors. In general, it is the transpiration process that is the main driving force carrying ions from the roots to the upper portions of the plant. The redistribution of substances once within the plant—plus simple and complex carbohydrates, amino acids, and proteins formed by photosynthetic activity—then becomes fairly complex, regulated by many interacting factors.

Uptake, Accumulation, and Redistribution versus Time

The uptake of various elements and their distribution and redistribution within the plant is governed by time. For example, shortly after germination

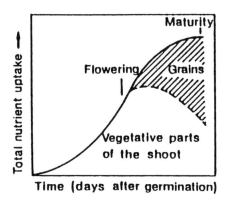

FIGURE 1.5 Total nutrient uptake with time (Marschner, 1986).

in soil, the Al concentration (frequently Fe also) found in the plant can be very high—at a concentration of Al that would be considered toxic for the more mature plant—although the newly forming plant seems unaffected. But within a few weeks after germination, the Al content in the plant declines sharply.

There seems to be an N form preference during the early growth of some plants for the ammonium (NH_4) form of nitrogen versus nitrate (NO_3). With time, this preference declines, and as the plant approaches maturity, NO_3 may begin to accumulate in the plant to fairly high concentrations if there is a substantial N supply in the rooting medium.

In general, during rapid vegetative growth and development, the uptake of elements from the rooting medium is substantial, and as the plant approaches maturity, the rate of accumulation begins to decline, as is illustrated in Figure 1.5.

During the reproductive (flowering and seed and/or fruit development) period, considerable redistribution of elements accrues, although the rate and extent varies with element. Thus, the elements can be classified by their mobility within the plant from the most to the least:

*   Very mobile: Mg, N, P, and K
*   Slightly mobile: S
*   Immobile: Cu, Fe, Mo, and Zn
*   Very immobile: B and Ca

The mobility characteristics of these elements will define in what portion of the plant one would expect deficiency symptoms to appear, the most mobile occurring in the older leaves, and the least mobile in the newly emerging and young leaves. Fruit disorders that are associated with either B or Ca (blossom-end rot, for example) occur because of their inadequate supply as well as their very immobile characteristic which restricts movement from other portions of the plant, even though sufficient levels exist, into the fruit.

As the plant matures, reduced uptake and redistribution results in large changes in the concentration of the elements found in the older and younger portions of the plant. With maturity, for example, the nitrogen (N), phosphorus (P), and potassium (K) content in leaves declines, while the calcium (Ca) and magnesium (Mg) content increases. These changes are the result of two factors, movement out of the maturing leaves for the mobile elements and a decrease in dry weight (loss of soluble carbohydrates), which affects the relative relationship that exists between mineral and organic contents.

These relative changes with time become important factors when assaying the plant to determine its nutrient-element status. Therefore, the time and plant part selected for analysis and evaluation are important considerations when conducting either a plant analysis or tissue test (see Chapters 5 and 6).

Diagnostic Plant Symptoms of Nutrient Element Insufficiencies

When a nutrient element insufficiency (deficiency and/or toxicity) occurs, visual symptoms may or may not appear, although normal plant development will be slowed. When visual symptoms do occur, such symptoms can frequently be used to identify the source of the insufficiency.

Deficiency Symptoms

Visual symptoms of deficiency may take various forms, such as:

- stunted or reduced growth of the entire plant with the plant itself either remaining green or lacking an over-all green color with either the older or younger leaves being light green to yellow in color.
- chlorosis of leaves, either interveinal or of the whole leaf itself, with symptoms either on the younger and/or older leaves, or both (chlorosis is due to the loss or lack of chlorophyll production).

- necrosis or death of a portion (margins or interveinal areas) of a leaf, or the whole leaf, usually occurring on the older leaves.
- slow or stunted growth of terminals (rosetting), the lack of terminal growth, or death of the terminal portions of the plant.
- a reddish purpling of leaves, frequently more intense on the underside of older leaves due to the accumulation of anthocyanin.

Toxicity Symptoms

Visual symptoms of toxicity may not always be the direct effect of the element in excess on the plant, but the effect of the excess element on one or more other elements. For example, an excessive level of potassium (K) in the plant can result in either a magnesium (Mg) and/or calcium (Ca) deficiency, excess phosphorus (P) can result in a zinc (Zn) deficiency, and excess Zn in an iron (Fe) deficiency.

These effects would compare to elements, such as boron (B), chlorine(Cl), copper (Cu), and maganese (Mn), which create visual symptoms that are the direct effect of an excess of that element present in the plant.

Some elements, such as aluminum (Al) and copper (Cu) can affect plant growth and development due to their toxic effect on root development and function.

A summary of general deficiency and toxicity symptoms are given in Table 1.13.

Hidden Hunger

In some instances, a nutrient element insufficiency may be such that no symptoms of stress will visually appear with the plant seeming to be developing normally. This condition has been named *hidden hunger*, a condition that can be uncovered by means of either a plant analysis and/or tissue test (see Chapters 4 and 5).

A *hidden hunger* occurrence frequently effects the final yield and the quality of the product produced. For grain crops, the grain yield and quality may be less than expected; for fruit crops, abnormalities, such as blossom-end rot and internal abnormalities may occur, and the post harvest characteristics of fruits and flowers will result in poor shipping quality and reduced longevity. Another example is potassium (K) insufficency in corn, a deficiency that is not evident until at maturity when plants easily lodge.

TABLE 1.13   Generalized Visual Leaf and Plant Nutrient Element Deficiency and Excess Symptoms

Element/status	Visual symptoms
Nitrogen (N)	
Deficiency	Light green leaf and plant color with the older leaves turning yellow, leaves that will eventually turn brown and die. Plant growth is slow, plants will be stunted, and will mature early.
Excess	Plants will be dark green in color and new growth will be succulent; susceptible if subjected to disease and insect infestation; and subjected to drought stress, plants will easily lodge. Blossom abortion and lack of fruit set will occur.
Ammonium toxicity	Plants fertilized with ammonium-nitrogen (NH_4-N) may exhibit ammonium-toxicity symptoms, with carbohydrate depletion and reduced plant growth. Lesions may occur on plant stems, there may be a downward cupping of the leaves, and a decay of the conductive tissue at the base of the stem with wilting of the plants under moisture stress. Blossom-end rot of fruit will occur and Mg deficiency symptoms may also occur.
Phosphorus (P)	
Deficiency	Plant growth will be slow and stunted, and the older leaves will have a purple coloration, particularly on the underside.
Excess	Phosphorus excess will not have a direct effect on the plant but may show visual deficiencies of Zn, Fe, and Mn. High P may also interfere with the normal Ca nutrition, with typical Ca deficiency symptoms occurring.
Potassium (K)	
Deficiency	On the older leaves, the edges will look burned, a symptom known as *scorch.*. Plants will easily lodge and be sensitive to disease infestation. Fruit and seed production will be impaired and of poor quality.
Excess	Plants will exhibit typical Mg, and possibly Ca deficiency symptoms due to a cation imbalance.
Calcium (Ca)	
Deficiency	The growing tips of roots and leaves will turn brown and die. The edges of the leaves will look ragged as the edges of emerging leaves stick together. Fruit quality will be affected with the occurrence of blossom-end rot on fruits.
Excess	Plants may exhibit typical Mg deficiency symptoms, and when in high excess, K deficiency may also occur.
Magnesium (Mg)	
Deficiency	Older leaves will be yellow in color with interveinal chlorosis (yellowing between the veins) symptoms. Plant growth will be slow and some plants may be easily infested by disease.
Excess	Results in a cation imbalance showing signs of either a Ca or K deficiency.

TABLE 1.13 Continued

Sulfur (S)

Deficiency	A general overall light green color of the entire plant with the older leaves being light green to yellow in color as the deficiency intensifies.
Excess	A premature senescence of leaves may occur.

Boron (B)

Deficiency	Abnormal development of the growing points (meristematic tissue) with the apical growing points eventually becoming stunted and dying. Flowers and fruits will abort. For some grain and fruit crops, yield and quality is significantly reduced
Excess	Leaf tips and margins will turn brown and die.

Chlorine (Cl)

Deficiency	Younger leaves will be chlorotic and plants will easily wilt. For wheat, a plant disease will infest the plant when Cl is deficient.
Excess	Premature yellowing of the lower leaves with burning of the leaf margins and tips. Leaf abscission will occur and plants will easily wilt.

Copper (Cu)

Deficiency	Plant growth will be slow and plants stunted with distortion of the young leaves and death of the growing point.
Excess	An Fe deficiency may be induced with very slow growth. Roots may be stunted.

Iron (Fe)

Deficiency	Interveinal chlorosis will occur on the emerging and young leaves with eventual *bleaching* of the new growth. When severe, the entire plant may be light green in color.
Excess	A bronzing of leaves with tiny brown spots on the leaves, a typical symptom frequently occurring with rice.

Manganese (Mn)

Deficiency	Interveinal chlorosis of young leaves while the leaves and plants remain generally green in color. When severe, the plants will be stunted.
Excess	Older leaves will show brown spots surrounded by a chlorotic zone and circle.

Molybdenum (Mo)

Deficiency	Symptoms will frequently appear similar to N deficiency. Older and middle leaves become chlorotic first, and in some instances, leaf margins are rolled and growth and flower formation are restricted.
Excess	Not of common occurrence.

Zinc (Zn)

Deficiency	Upper leaves will show interveinal chlorosis with an eventual whiting of the affected leaves. Leaves may be small and distorted with a rosette form.
Excess	An Fe deficiency will develop.

Climatic and Other Causes

The occurrence of the symptoms may not necessarily be the direct effect of a nutrient element insufficiency. For example, stunted and slowed plant growth and the purpling of leaves can be the result of climatic stress, cool air and/or root temperatures, lack of adequate moisture, etc. Damage due to wind, insects, disease, and applied foliar chemicals can produce visual symptoms typical of a nutrient element insufficiency. Some nutrient element deficiencies have been classed as *physiological diseases* as given in Table 1.14. In all these cases, carefully followed diagnostic techniques must be employed—particularly the use of plant analyses and/or tissue tests (see Chapters 4 and 5)—if the cause for visual disorders are to be correctly identified.

Other Effects

A nutrient element insufficiency (deficiency or excess) can make the plant sensitive to climatic stress, and/or be easily subjected to insect and disease infestations. A high nitrogen (N) level in the plant can make the plant sensitive to moisture stress and easily susceptible to insect and desease infestations. If ammonium-nitrogen (NH4-N) is the primary source of nitrogen (N), symptoms of NH4 toxicity, fruit disorders, and the decay of conductive tissues may occur.

Some fungus diseases are more likely to occur on plants that are marginally deficient in a particular element, an example being the occurrence of powdery mildew on leaves of greenhouse-grown cucumber when magnesium (Mg) is not fully sufficient. Wheat that is insufficient in chlorine (Cl) is easily susceptible to a disease called *take-all*.

Although not generally considered an essential element, the lack of adequate silicon (Si) in rice (possibly true of other small grains also), the plants lack stem strength and will easily lodge. Silicon insufficiency has also been suggested as a probable cause for disease infestations in rice as well as other crop species. The presence of Si in plant leaves provides a barrier to the evasion of fungus hyphae into leaf cellular structures.

TABLE 1.14   Physiological Disorders that Are Elemental Deficiencies

Deficient element	Disorder	Crop	Symptoms
Boron (B)	Raan (brown heart)	Swede, turnip	Rotting of center of root
	Heart rot	Beets	Death of center of crown, rotting of center of root
	Hollow stem	Cauliflower	Rotting of center of stem
	Bitter pit	Apple	Decay or corking of the flesh under the skin
Calcium (Ca)	Blossom-end rot	Tomato, pepper	Decay of the blossom-end of of the fruit
Chloride (Cl)	Take-all	Wheat	Root rot
Copper (Cu)	Wither tip	Cereals	Chlorosis of leaves, withering of tips of leaves and inflorescences
Manganese (Mn)	Grey speck	Oat	Irregular grey-brown streaks or specks on leaves
	Speckled yellows	Sugar beet	Chlorosis between leaf veins, inward curling of leaves
	Marsh spot	Pea	Brown area in center of seed
	Little leaf	Apple	Small, malformed leaves, shortened internodes
Molybdenum (Mo)	Whiptail	Cauliflower	Reduction of suppression of leaf blades

CHAPTER 2

The Major Elements

Terminology

The nine major elements, carbon (C), nitrogen (N), oxygen (O), phosphorus (P), hydrogen (H), potassium (K), calcium (Ca), magnesium (Mg), and sulfur (S) have been so designated because they are found and required in substantial concentrations compared to the other seven essential elements, which have been designated as the micronutrients (see Tables 1.2 and 3.1).

These nine major elements are given in percent concentrations, although they can be expressed in SI units as grams per kilogram (mg/kg), centimole (p+) per kilogram [cmol (p+)/kg], or centimole per kilogram (cmol/kg). These unit comparisons are shown for five of the major elements (levels were selected for illustrative purposes):

Element	Percent	g/kg	cmol(p+)/kg	cmol/kg
P	0.32	3.2	—	10
K	1.95	19.5	50	50
Ca	2.00	20.0	25	50
Mg	0.48	4.8	10	20
S	0.32	3.2	—	10

There are other designations that are currently used or have been used in the past for several of the major elements. For example, N, P, and K are frequently referred to as the *fertilizer* elements because N, P, and K are the primary elements in chemical fertilizers (in fertilizers, the P and K contents are usually given as their oxides, P_2O_5 and K_2O).

In the past, Ca, Mg, and S have been called *secondary* elements, a term that is no longer accepted for identifying these three major elements.

Carbon, Hydrogen, and Oxygen

These three major elements are combined in green plants in the process called *photosynthesis* (see Figure 1.1), the conversion of light energy to chemical energy. For active photosynthesis to take place:

- The plant must be fully turgid (not under water stress).
- The stomata must be open, which enhances gaseous exchange so that carbon dioxide (CO_2) can readily enter plant leaves.
- The leaf surface must be exposed to full sunlight.
- The plant must be nutritionally sound.

Magnesium and P play direct roles in photosynthesis as well as the micronutrient iron (Fe). If these elements are not present at their sufficiency levels, photosynthetic activity will be significantly reduced.

Nitrogen

Functions in Plants—Nitrogen is found in both inorganic and organic forms in the plant, and combines with C, H, O, and sometimes S to form amino acids, amino enzymes, nucleic acids, chlorophyll, alkaloids, and purine bases. Although inorganic N can accumulate in the plant, primarily in stems and conductive tissue in the nitrate (NO_3) form, organic N predominates as high molecular weight proteins in plants.

Content and Distribution—Nitrogen consists of 1.50 to 6.00% of the dry weight of many crops with sufficiency values from 2.50 to 3.50% in leaf tissue. A lower range of 1.80 to 2.20% is found in most fruit crops and a higher range of 4.80 to 5.50% is found in legume species. Critical values vary considerably, depending on crop species, stage of growth, and plant part. Highest concentrations are found in new leaves, with the total plant N content normally decreasing with the age of the plant or any one of its parts. A list of sufficiency ranges for N in a selected number of crops is given in Table 2.1.

TABLE 2.1 Sufficiency Range for Nitrogen in Selected Crops

Crop	Plant part	Sampling time	Sufficiency range (% N)
Field crops			
Alfalfa	Top 6 inches	First flower	4.50–5.00
Corn	Ear leaf	Initial silk	2.70–4.00
Peanut	Upper part of plant	Early pegging	3.50–4.50
Rice	Most recent leaf	Panicle initiation	2.60–3.20
Soybean	Most recent leaf	Prior to pod set	4.00–5.50
Winter wheat	Top two leaves	Just before heading	1.75–3.00
Vegetables			
Bean, snap	Upper developed leaves	Initial pod set	5.00–6.00
Cucumber, field	Fifth leaf from top	Flower to small fruit set	4.50–6.00
Lettuce, cos type	Wrapper leaf	Mature	3.50–4.50
Potato, Irish	Upper developed leaf	30-cm tall	3.00–4.00
Tomato, field	Adjacent top inflorescence	Mid-bloom	4.00–6.00
Watermelon	Fifth leaf from top	Flower start, small fruit	4.00–5.00
Fruits and nuts			
Apple	Mid-shoot current growth	Mid-season	1.90–2.60
Banana	Six- to nine-month-old leaves		3.50–4.50
Grape	Petiole opposite basal flower cluster	Full bloom	1.60–2.80
Olive	Mid-shoot		1.50–2.50
Orange	Behind fruit	Five- to seven-month-old leaves	2.20–3.50
Peach	Fruiting or non-fruiting spurs	Mid-summer	3.00–3.50
Pecan	Mid-portion terminal growth	56 to 84 days after terminal growth	2.70–3.50

Ammonium (NH_4)-fertilized plants are usually higher in Kjeldahl N than are those that have mostly NO_3-N available for adsorption. High-yielding crops will contain from 50 to 500 lbs N/A (56 to 560 kg N/ha), with the extent of removal dependent on the disposition of the crop.

The relationship between N and P in plants is well known, as is the relationship between N and K. The ratios of N and P and N and K are used as DRIS norms for interpreting a plant analysis result.

The uptake of NO_3 stimulates the uptake of cations, while chloride (Cl^-) and hydroxyl (OH^-) anions restrict NO_3^- anion uptake. High carbohydrate status enhances the uptake of ammonium (NH_4), and the uptake of NH_4 restricts cations which can lead to Ca deficiency, as well as to reduced K levels in the plant.

Nitrogen exists as the nitrate (NO_3^-) anion in main stems and leaf petioles, ranging in concentration from 8,000 to 12,000 ppm during early growth, and declines to the range from 3,000 to 8,000 ppm in mid-season. It is most concentrated at the base of the main stem and in the petioles of recently fully matured leaves. The determination of NO_3 in either stem or petiole tissue is used as a means of determining the N status of plants or as a means of regulating N supplemental fertilizer applications. Nitrate sufficiency ranges for a number of vegetable crops are given in Table 2.2.

Soluble amino acids are also found in the plant.

Available Forms for Root Absorption—Nitrogen exists in the soil as either the NO_3^- anion or the ammonium (NH_4^+) cation, the uptake of either form influenced by soil pH, temperature, and the presence of other ions in the soil solution. The NH_4^+ cation participates in cation exchange within the soil. Nitrite (NO_2^-) may be present in the soil solution under anaerobic conditions and is toxic to plants at very low levels (less than 5 ppm).

Movement in Soil and Root Absorption—Nitrogen as the NO_3^- anion moves in the soil primarily by mass flow with most of the NO_3 absorbed when it reaches the root surface. Nitrate ions can be readily leached from the rooting zone by irrigation water and/or rainfall, or lifted into the rooting

TABLE 2.2 Critical Nitrate-Nitrogen Concentrations at a 10% Growth Restriction for Various Vegetable Crops

Crop	Sampling time	Plant part	NO_3-N, ppm
Cucumber	42 days from seeding	Mature petioles	2,000
Lettuce	Market maturity	Entire aerial portion	2,000
Potato	18 days vegetative growth	Petiole from terminal	12,000
Radish	Market maturity	Root	500
Spinach	Market maturity	Entire aerial portion	1,700
Squash	42 days from seeding	Mature petiole	1,000
Sweet melon	42 days from seeding	Mature petiole	3,000
Tomato	46 days from seeding	Petiole 2 from terminal	500

From Maynard, D.N., A.V. Barker, P.L. Minotti, and N.H. Peck. 1976. Nitrate accumulation in vegetables. *Adv. Agron.* 28:71–118. With permission.

zone by upward moving water being driven by water loss as a result of evaporation at the soil surface and/or evapotranspiration by plants.

The other N form, the ammonium NH_4^+ cation, acts much like the potassium (K^+) cation in the soil and its movement in the soil solution is primarily by diffusion.

Deficiency Symptoms—Plants deficient in N are very slow growing, weak, and stunted. Typically, the plants are light green to yellow in foliage color. The initial and more severe symptoms of yellow-leaf deficiency are seen in the older leaves, since N is mobilized in the older tissue for transport to the actively growing portions of the plant. Nitrogen-deficient plants will mature early with yield and quality significantly reduced.

Excess (Toxicity) Symptoms—Plants with an excess of N are dark green in color with succulent foliage, which is easily susceptible to disease and insect invasion. The plants may lodge easily, are susceptible to drought stress, and fruit and seed crops may fail to yield. Produced fruit and grain will be of poor quality.

If NH_4 is the only or major form of N available for plant uptake, a toxicity condition may develop that results in a breakdown of vascular tissue, thereby restricting water uptake. The fruit of fruiting crops (i.e., tomato, pepper, cucumber) may develop blossom-end rot symptoms, or fruit set may be poor. Symptoms of Ca deficiency may occur if NH_4 is the primary source of N. Carbohydrate depletion can occur with NH_4 nutrition, which results in growth reduction.

Fertilizer Sources—A crop response to applied mineral N fertilizer would be expected to be similar irrespective of the N source, if applied as directed. However, the efficiency of N utilization will vary with time, method of application, and N form. A side effect of N fertilizer application is the acidifying effect of ammonium-form fertilizers (see Table 2.3). A list of commonly used N fertilizers is given in Table 2.4.

Phosphorus

Functions in Plants—Phosphorus is a component of certain enzymes and proteins, adenosine triphosphate (ATP), ribonucleic acids (RNA), deoxyribonucleic acids (DNA), and phytin. ATP is involved in various energy transfer reactions, and RNA and DNA are components of genetic information.

TABLE 2.3   Soil Acidification by Nitrogen Fertilizers (IFA World Fertilizer Use Manual, 1992)

Nitrogen fertilizer	Amount of CaO to compensate the soil acidification induced by 2.2 lb (1 kg) nitrogen[a]
Calcium ammonium nitrate (27% N)	1.32 lb (0.6 kg)
Ammonia, urea, and ammonium nitrate	2.2 lb (1 kg)
Diammonium phosphate and ammonium nitrate	4.4 lb (2 kg)
Ammonium sulfate	6.6 lb (3 kg)

[a] On the basis of 50% utilization rate.

TABLE 2.4   Nitrogen-Containing Fertilizers, Their Formula, Form, and Nitrogen Content

Name	Formula	Form	% N
Inorganic			
Ammonium nitrate	NH_4NO_3	Solid	34
Ammonium sulfate	$(NH_4)_2SO_4$	Solid	21
Ammonium thiosulfate	$(NH_4)_2S_2O_3$	Liquid	12
Anhydrous ammonia	NH_3	Gas	82
Aqua ammonia	NH_4OH	Liquid	20–25
Nitrogen solutions	(varies)	Liquid	19–32
Monoammonium phosphate	$NH_4H_2PO_4$	Solid	11
Diammonium phosphate	$(NH_4)_2HPO_4$	Solid	16–18
Calcium cyanamide	$CaCN_2$	Solid	21
Calcium nitrate	$Ca(NO_3)_2$	Solid	16
Sodium nitrate	$NaNO_3$	Solid	16
Potassium nitrate	KNO_3	Solid	13
Synthetic organic			
Urea	$CO(NH_2)_2$	Solid	45–46
Sulfur-coated urea	$CO(NH_2)_2$-S	Solid	40
Urea-formaldehyde	$CO(NH_2)_2$-CH_2O	Solid	38
Natural organic			
Cotton seed meal		Solid	12–13
Milorganite		Solid	12
Animal manure		Solid	10–12
Sewage sludge		Solid	10–20
Chicken litter		Solid	20–40

Content and Distribution in Plants—Phosphorus consists of 0.15 to 1.00% of the dry weight of most plants with sufficiency values from 0.20 to 0.40% in recently mature leaf tissue. Critical values for P are normally less than 0.20% (when deficient) and greater than 1.00% (when in excess). The P content in leaves tends to decrease with age. Sufficiency ranges for P in a variety of crops are given in Table 2.5.

TABLE 2.5 Sufficiency Range for Phosphorus in Selected Crops

Crop	Plant part	Sampling time	Sufficiency range (% P)
Field crops			
Alfalfa	Top 6 inches	First flower	0.26–0.70
Corn	Ear leaf	Initial silk	0.25–0.50
Peanut	Upper part of plant	Early pegging	0.20–0.35
Rice	Most recent leaf	Panicle initiation	0.09–0.18
Soybean	Most recent leaf	Prior to pod set	0.26–0.50
Winter wheat	Top two leaves	Just before heading	0.21–0.50
Vegetables			
Bean, snap	Upper developed leaves	Initial pod set	0.35–0.75
Cucumber, field	Fifth leaf from top	Flower to small fruit set	0.34–0.75
Lettuce, Cos type	Wrapper leaf	Mature	0.40–0.80
Potato, Irish	Upper developed leaf	30-cm tall	0.25–0.40
Tomato, field	Adjacent top inflorescence	Mid-bloom	0.25–0.75
Watermelon	Fifth leaf from top	Flower start, small fruit	0.30–0.80
Fruits and nuts			
Apple	Mid-shoot current growth	Mid-season	0.14–0.40
Banana	Six- to nine-month-old leaves		0.29–0.40
Grape	Petioles, opposite basal flower cluster	Full bloom	0.30–0.60
Olive	Mid-shoot		0.10–0.30
Orange	Behind fruit	Five- to seven-month-old leaves	0.12–0.50
Peach	Fruiting or non-fruiting spurs	Mid-summer	0.14–0.25
Pecan	Mid-portion terminal growth	56 to 84 days after terminal growth	0.14–0.30

Highest concentration of P is found in new leaves and their petioles. High-yielding crops contain from 15 to 75 lbs P/A (17 to 84 kg P/ha). The amount of P present when crops are harvested will be considerably less for grain crops when only the grain is removed, leaving behind most of the P in the remainder of the plant.

The relationship between N and P is well known, as is the relationship between P and copper (Cu), Fe, manganese (Mn), and zinc (Zn). Ratios of 3 to 1 between N and P, and 200 to 1 between P and Zn are considered critical. The ratio of N to P is used as a DRIS norm for interpreting a plant analysis.

Soluble P (in 2% acetic acid) is present as the orthophosphate (PO_4^{3-}) anion in main stems and leaf petioles of the actively growing portions of the plant. Its concentration ranges from 100 to 5,000 ppm of the dry weight and can be used to evaluate the P status of the plant. Critical concentrations occur at approximately 2,500 ppm. A list of critical soluble P values for several crops are given in Table 2.6.

Available Forms for Root Absorption—Phosphorus exists in most soils in about equal amounts of organic or inorganic forms. Dihydrogen phosphate ($H_2PO_4^-$) and monohydrogen phosphate (HPO_4^{2-}) are the two anion forms of P, their ratio depending on soil pH. A combination of Al, Fe, or Ca phosphate is the major inorganic source of P; the relative amount among these three forms being a function of soil pH also.

Phosphorus is released into the soil solution with the decomposition of crop residues and microorganisms, thereby being a major source of P for plant utilization.

Movement in Soil and Root Absorption—The phosphate ($H_2PO_4^-$ and HPO_4^{2-}) anions are brought in contact with the root surface primarily by diffusion in the soil solution. However, root interception and the abundance of root hairs will significantly increase the opportunity for P absorption. Cool soil temperatures and low soil moisture content can reduce P uptake, and therefore create a P deficiency.

Deficiency Symptoms—Slow-growing, weak, and stunted plants that may be dark green in color with older leaves showing a purple pigmentation are symptomatic of P deficiency. Since P is fairly mobile in the plant, deficiency symptoms initially occur in the older tissue.

TABLE 2.6 Interpretative Phosphorus Tissue Analysis Values for Western Crops

Plant	Time of sampling	Plant part	Phosphorus level (ppm[a]) Deficient	Sufficient
Bean (bush, snap)	Mid-growth	Petiole of fourth leaf from growing tip	1,000	3,000
Cantaloupe	Early growth (short runners)	Petiole of sixth leaf from growing tip	2,000	4,000
Cucumber	Early fruit set (pickling)	Petiole of sixth leaf from leaf tip	1,500	2,500
Lettuce	At harvest	Mid-rib of wrapper leaf	1,500	2,500
Pepper, sweet	Early growth	Petiole of young, mature leaf	2,000	4,000
Potato	Early season	Petiole of fourth leaf from growing tip	1,200	2,000
Sweet corn	Tasseling	Mid-rib of first leaf above primary ear	500	1,000
Tomato (canning)	Fruit 1" diameter	Petiole of fourth leaf from growing tip	2,000	13,000
Watermelon	Early fruit	Petiole of sixth leaf from growing tip	1,500	2,500

[a] P = acetic acid-soluble PO_4-P.

From Ludwick, A.E. (ed.). 1990. *Western Fertilizer Handbook-Horticultural Edition.* Interstate Publishers, Inc., Danville, Il.

Excess (Toxicity) Symptoms—An excess of P appears mainly in the form of a micronutrient deficiency, with either Fe or Zn being the first elements to be affected. High P may also interfere with the normal metabolism of the plant. Phosphorus leaf contents greater than 100% would be considered toxic.

Fertilizer Sources—Phosphorus fertilizers vary considerably in their water solubility, which can affect crop response. Method of application (broadcast versus row) will also influence availability as applied P can be readily fixed by the soil into unavailable forms. A list of P-containing fertilizers are given in Table 2.7.

**TABLE 2.7 Phosphorus-Containing Fertilizers, Their Formula, and
Phosphate Content**

| | | % P_2O_5 (available) | |
Name	Formula	Citrate soluble	Water soluble
20% superphosphate (0-20-0)	$Ca(H_2PO_4)_2$	16–22	90
Concentrated superphosphate (0-45-0)	$Ca(H_2PO_4)_2$	44–52	95–98
Monoammonium phosphate	$NH_4H_2PO_4$	48	100
Diammonium phosphate	$(NH_4)_2HPO_4$	46–48	100
Ammonium polyphosphate	$(NH_4)_3HP_2O_7 \cdot H_2O$	34	100
Phosphoric acid	H_3PO_4	55	100
Superphosphoric acid, polyphosphate	$H_3PO_4 + H_4P_2O_7$	76–85	100
Rock phosphate	Fluoro- and chloroapatites		
	$3Ca_3(PO_4)_2 \cdot CaF_2$	3–26	0
Basic slag	$5CaO \cdot P_2O_5 \cdot SiO_2$	2–16	—
Bone meal		22–28	—

Potassium

Functions in Plants—Potassium is involved in maintaining the water status
of the plant, the turgor pressure of its cells, and the opening and closing of
its stomata. Potassium is required for the accumulation and translocation of
newly formed carbohydrates.

Content and Distribution in Plants—Potassium consists of 1.00 to 5.00%
of the dry weight of leaf tissue with sufficiency values from 1.50 to 3.00%
in recently mature leaf tissue for many crops. Potassium content is considered deficient or in excess when K critical values are less than 1.50% or
greater than 5.00%, respectively. When in excess, K levels may exceed the
sufficiency level two- to three-fold. Sufficient K can be as high as 6.00 to
8.00% in the stem tissue of some vegetable crops. Highest concentrations
are found in new leaves, their petioles, and plant stems. The K content of
leaves decreases with age. The sufficiency ranges for a number of crops are
given in Table 2.8.

High-yielding crops contain from 50 to 500 lbs K/A (56 to 560 kg/ha),

TABLE 2.8 Sufficiency Range for Potassium in Selected Crops

Crop	Plant part	Sampling time	Sufficiency range (% K)
Field crops			
Alfalfa	Top 6 inches	First flower	2.00–3.50
Corn	Ear leaf	Initial silk	1.70–3.00
Peanut	Upper part of plant	Early pegging	1.70–3.00
Rice	Most recent leaf	Panicle initiation	1.00–2.20
Soybean	Most recent leaf	Prior to pod set	1.70–2.50
Winter wheat	Top two leaves	Just before heading	1.50–3.00
Vegetables			
Bean, snap	Upper developed leaves	Initial pod set	2.25–4.00
Cucumber, field	Fifth leaf from top	Flower to small fruit set	3.90–5.00
Lettuce, cos type	Wrapper leaf	Mature	5.50–6.20
Potato, Irish	Upper developed leaf	30-cm tall	6.00–8.00
Tomato, field	Adjacent top inflorescence	Mid-bloom	2.90–5.00
Watermelon	Fifth leaf from top	Flower start, small fruit	4.00–5.00
Fruits and nuts			
Apple	Mid-shoot current growth	Mid-season	1.50–2.00
Banana	Six- to nine-month-old leaves		3.80–5.00
Grape	Petioles, opposite basal flower cluster	Full bloom	2.50–5.00
Olive	Mid-shoot		0.90–1.20
Orange	Behind fruit	Five- to seven-month-old leaves	1.20–3.00
Peach	Fruiting or non-fruiting spurs	Mid-summer	2.00–3.00
Pecan	Mid-portion terminal growth	56 to 84 day after terminal growth	1.25–2.50

with crops such as banana containing 1,500 lbs/A (1,680 kg/ha). Most plants will absorb more K than they need. This excess is frequently referred to as *luxury consumption*. The harvest of most fruits removes sizable quantities of K from the soil.

The relationship between K and Mg is well known, as is the relationship between K and Ca. High K concentrations first result in a Mg deficiency; when K is in greater imbalance, they will cause a Ca deficiency. The K to

Mg and K to Ca ratios are used as DRIS norms for interpreting a plant analysis result. Ammonium (NH_4^+) cations can also play a role in the balance that exists among the three cations, K^+, Ca^{2+}, and Mg^{2+}.

Since K does not exist in a combined form in the plant, it can be extracted easily from either fresh or dried tissue. The extracted concentration is essentially equal to that determined by total analysis. Some vegetable crops are considered deficient when extracted sap from fresh stems and petioles contain less than 2,000 ppm K, and adequate when the K content is greater than 3,000 ppm.

Available Forms for Root Absorption—Potassium exists in the soil in four forms:

- As the K^+ cation in the soil solution
- As exchangeable K^+ on soil colloids
- As fixed K in the lattice of 2:1 clays
- As a component in K-bearing minerals.

An equilibrium exists between K in the soil solution, exchangeable K, and fixed K (see Figure 2.1). When K fertilizer is applied to the soil, the

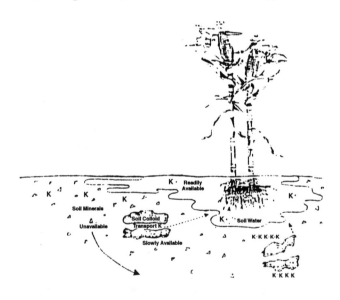

FIGURE 2.1 Potassium equilibrium in the soil between that in the soil solution, exchangeable, and fixed.

equilibrium shifts toward exchangeable and fixed K, a shift which is reversed as K is removed from the soil solution by root absorption.

As the anion concentration increases in the soil solution, the K level also increases. Although the balance of Ca and Mg to K in the plant is important, K uptake is not significantly affected by soil Ca levels since Ca moves in the soil primarily by mass flow, while K moves by diffusion.

Movement in Soil and Root Absorption—Potassium moves to the root-absorbing surface by diffusion in the soil solution, the rate of diffusion highly temperature dependent. The extent of root contact (root density) with the soil also has a significant effect on uptake. Soil oxygen (O_2) has a greater effect on K uptake than for most other ions.

Deficiency Symptoms—Plants deficient in K will lodge easily, are sensitive to disease infestation, fruit yield and quality will be reduced, and older leaves will look as if they had been burned along the edges, a deficiency symptom known as *scorch*. Since K is mobile in the plant, deficiency symptoms first appear in the older tissue. Potassium-deficient plants may also become sensitive to the presence of ammonium (NH_4), leading to a possible NH_4 toxicity syndrome.

Excess (Toxicity) Symptoms—Plants with an excess of K will become deficient in Mg and possibly Ca, due to the imbalance. A Mg deficiency is most likely to occur first.

Fertilizer Sources—A list of fertilizer sources for K is given in Table 2.9.

TABLE 2.9 Potassium-Containing Fertilizers, Their Formula, and Potassium Oxide Content

Carrier	Formula	% K_2O
Potassium chloride (muriate of potash)	KCl	60–63
Potassium sulfate	K_2SO_4	50–52
Potassium magnesium sulfate (SUL-PO-MAG)	$K_2SO_4 \cdot MgSO_4$	22
Potassium nitrate	KNO_3	44
Potassium hydroxide	KOH	83

Calcium

Functions in Plants—Calcium plays an important part in maintaining cell integrity and membrane permeability, enhances pollen germination and growth, and activates a number of enzymes for cell mitosis, division, and elongation. Calcium may also be important for protein synthesis and carbohydrate transfer, and its presence may serve to detoxify the presence of heavy metals in the plant.

Content and Distribution in Plants—Calcium content in plants ranges between 0.20 to 5.00% of the dry weight in leaf tissue, with sufficiency values from 0.30 to 3.00% in leaf tissue of most crops. Critical values for Ca vary considerably among various crop species, lowest for the grain crops and highest for some vegetable and most fruit crops. Highest concentrations are found in older leaves as the Ca content of leaves tends to increase with age. Sufficiency ranges for a number of crops are given in Table 2.10.

High-yielding crops contain from 10 to 175 lbs Ca/A (11 to 196 kg Ca/ha). Calcium removal will be considerably less for grain and most fruit crops when only the grain or fruit is removed, leaving behind the plant which contains most of the Ca.

The relationship between Ca and K is as well known as that between Ca and Mg. These ratios are used as DRIS norms for the interpretation of a plant analysis result. The ratio of Ca to N in fruit crops and a similar ratio between Ca and boron (B) may be related to quality. Ammonium nutrition can create a Ca deficiency by reducing Ca uptake.

It has been suggested that total Ca content does not relate to sufficiency, since Ca accumulates in some plants as crystals of calcium oxalate. Therefore, extractable Ca (in 2% acetic acid) may be a better indicator of sufficiency. The critical Ca concentration for soluble Ca is around 800 ppm, a concentration of Ca which has been suggested as the true *critical* value for most plants.

It is generally assumed that if the soil pH is within the acceptable range in the rooting media, Ca should be of sufficient concentration to ensure plant-Ca sufficiency, assuming that other factors are also within normal range. However, soil pH seems to have little effect on Ca uptake.

Available Forms for Root Absorption—Calcium exists as the Ca^{2+} cation in the soil solution and as exchangeable Ca on soil colloids. Usually Ca is

TABLE 2.10 Sufficiency Range for Calcium in Selected Crops

Crop	Plant part	Sampling time	Sufficiency range (% Ca)
Field crops			
Alfalfa	Top 6 inches	First flower	1.80–3.00
Corn	Ear leaf	Initial silk	0.21–1.00
Peanut	Upper part of plant	Early pegging	1.25–1.75
Rice	Most recent leaf	Panicle initiation	1.00–4.00
Soybean	Most recent leaf	Prior to pod set	1.35–2.00
Winter wheat	Top two leaves	Just before heading	0.21–1.00
Vegetables			
Bean, snap	Upper developed leaves	Initial pod set	1.50–2.50
Cucumber, field	Fifth leaf from top	Flower to small fruit set	1.40–3.50
Lettuce, Cos type	Wrapper leaf	Mature	2.00–2.80
Potato, Irish	Upper developed leaf	30-cm tall	1.00–2.50
Tomato, field	Adjacent top inflorescence	Mid-bloom	1.00–3.00
Watermelon	Fifth leaf from top	Flower start, small fruit	1.70–3.00
Fruits and nuts			
Apple	Mid-shoot current growth	Mid-season	1.20–1.60
Banana	Six- to nine-month-old leaves		0.80–1.50
Grape	Petiole, opposite basal flower cluster	Full bloom	0.42–1.30
Olive	Mid–shoot		1.00+
Orange	Behind fruit	Five- to seven-month-old leaves	1.10–4.00
Peach	Fruiting or non-fruiting spurs	Mid-summer	1.80–2.70
Pecan	Mid-portion terminal growth	56 to 84 days after terminal growth	1.00–1.75

the cation of highest concentration in the soil in both soluble and exchangeable forms for soils high in pH (>8.0), soils which may contain sizable quantities of Ca as precipitates of calcium carbonate ($CaCO_3$) and calcium sulfate ($CaSO_4$).

Movement in Soil and Root Absorption—Calcium moves in the soil by mass flow, the dominant supply factor, and diffusion. Therefore, Ca availability can be significantly affected by soil moisture level. Reduced plant evapotranspiration will also reduce the uptake of Ca by the plant

Deficiency Symptoms—The growing tips of roots and leaves of Ca deficient plants turn brown and die, a symptom frequently referred to as *tipburn*. Leaves curl and their margins turn brown with newly emerging leaves sticking together at the margins, leaving the expanded leaves shredded on their edges. Fruit quality will be reduced with a high incidence of blossom-end rot and internal decay.

Since Ca is an immobile element in the plant, deficiencies occur at the growing terminals, and in addition, reproduction may be delayed or terminated all together. The conductive tissue at the base of the plant will decay, resulting in the reduction of the uptake of water, wilting on high atmospheric demand days, and a reduction in essential element uptake.

Excess (Toxicity) Symptoms—Excessive Ca content will produce a deficiency of either Mg or K, depending on the concentration of these two elements in the plant.

Fertilizer Sources—For acid soils, it is generally assumed that maintaining the soil pH within the optimum range (5.8 to 7.5) by frequent liming will provide sufficient Ca to meet crop requirements. Sources of Ca for soil application are given in Table 2.11.

Magnesium

Functions in Plants—Magnesium is a component of the chlorophyll molecule (see Figure 1.2), serves as a cofactor in most enzymes that activate phosphorylation processes as a bridge between pyrophosphate structures of ATP or ADP and the enzyme molecule, and stabilizes the ribosome particles in the configuration for protein synthesis.

Content and Distribution—Magnesium plant content ranges between 0.15 to 1.00% of the dry weight in leaf tissue, with the sufficiency value being 0.25% in the leaf tissue of most crops. Critical values for Mg may vary among various crop species, being lowest for the grain crops and highest for legumes and some vegetable and fruit crops. The Mg content in leaves increases with age, the highest concentrations found in older leaves. The sufficiency ranges for a number of crops are given in Table 2.12.

TABLE 2.11   Calcium-Containing Carriers, Their Formula, and Calcium Content

Carrier	Formula	% Ca
Liming materials		
Blast furnace slag	$CaSiO_3$	29
Calcitic limestone	$CaCO_3$	32
Dolomitic limestone	$CaCO_3 + MgCO_3$	22
Hydrate lime	$Ca(OH)_2$	46
Precipitated lime	CaO	60
Fertilizers		
Calcium nitrate	$Ca(NO_3)_2$	19
Superphosphate, normal	$Ca(H_2PO_4)_2 + CaSO_4 \cdot 2H_2O$	20
Superphosphate, triple	$Ca(H_2PO_4)_2$	14
Others		
Gypsum	$CaSO_4 \cdot 2H_2O$	23
Gypsum (by-product)	$CaSO_4 \cdot 2H_2O$	17[a]
Gypsum (impure)	$CaSO_4 \cdot 2H_2O$	15[a]

[a] Calcium content varies.

High-yielding crops will contain from 10 to 175 lbs Mg/A (11 to 196 kg Mg/ha), with crop removal being considerably less for grain and some fruit crops when only the grain or fruit is removed, leaving behind most of the Mg that exists primarily in the plant itself.

The relationship between Mg and K is well known, as is the relationship between Mg and Ca. These ratios are used as DRIS norms for the interpretation of a plant analysis result. Magnesium deficiency can be induced by high concentrations of either the NH_4^+, K^+, or Ca^{2+} cations in the rooting medium, as the Mg^{2+} cation is the poorest competitor among all these cations.

There are some plant species or cultivars within species that have a particular sensitivity to Mg that will become Mg deficient under moisture and/or temperature stress even though Mg may be at sufficient availability levels in the rooting media.

Available Forms for Root Absorption—Magnesium exists as the Mg^{2+} cation in the soil solution and as exchangeable Mg on soil colloids, usually the cation being next to the highest in concentration in the soil in both

TABLE 2.12 Sufficiency Range for Magnesium in Selected Crops

Crop	Plant part	Sampling time	Sufficiency range (% Mg)
Field crops			
Alfalfa	Top 6 inches	First flower	0.30–1.00
Corn	Ear leaf	Initial silk	0.20–1.00
Peanut	Upper part of plant	Early pegging	0.30–0.80
Rice	Most recent leaf	Panicle initiation	0.20–0.30
Soybean	Most recent leaf	Prior to pod set	0.26–1.00
Winter wheat	Top two leaves	Just before heading	0.16–1.00
Vegetables			
Bean, snap	Upper developed leaves	Initial pod set	0.30–1.00
Cucumber, field	5th leaf from top	Flower to small fruit set	0.30–1.00
Lettuce, cos type	Wrapper leaf	Mature	0.60–0.80
Potato, Irish	Upper developed leaf	30-cm tall	0.70–1.00
Tomato, field	Adjacent top inflorescence	Mid-bloom	0.40–0.60
Watermelon	5th leaf from top	Flower start, small fruit	0.50–0.80
Fruits and nuts			
Apple	Mid-shoot current growth	Mid-season	0.25–0.40
Banana	6- to 9-month-old leaves		0.25–0.80
Grape	Petiole, opposite basal flower cluster	Full bloom	0.13–0.40
Olive	Mid-shoot		0.20+
Orange	Behind fruit	5- to 7-month-old leaves	1.10–4.00
Peach	Fruiting or non-fruiting spurs	Mid-summer	0.30–0.80
Pecan	Mid-portion terminal growth	56 to 84 days after terminal growth	0.30–0.60

soluble and exchangeable forms when the soil is slightly acid to neutral in pH. The availability of Mg declines significantly when the soil water pH is less than 5.4.

Movement in Soil and Root Absorption—The supply of Mg to the roots depends on root interception, mass flow, and diffusion, with mass flow being the primary delivery mechanism. Magnesium deficiency can occur under soil moisture stress even when the soil is adequate in available Mg.

Deficiency Symptoms—Plants deficient in Mg exhibit a yellowing of leaves or interveinal chlorosis, which begins on the older leaves as Mg is a mobile element in the plant. With an increased deficiency of Mg, symptoms will also appear on the younger leaves with the development of necrosis symptoms when the deficiency is very severe.

Excess (Toxicity) Symptoms—There are no specific toxicity symptoms as the Mg content of the plant can be quite high (>1.0%) in leaf tissue without inducing a deficiency of either Ca or K. However, an imbalance among these three elements, occurring when the Mg content in the plant is unusually high, may reduce growth.

Fertilizer Sources—For acid soils, and as for Ca, it is generally assumed that maintaining the soil pH within the optimum range (5.8 to 7.5) by frequent liming using dolomitic (Mg-bearing) limestone, or other high-content Mg liming materials, will provide sufficient Mg to meet crop requirements. Sources of Mg for soil application are given in Table 2.13.

Sulfur

Functions in Plants—Sulfur is involved in protein synthesis and is part of the amino acids, cystine and thiamine. Sulfur is present in peptide glutathione, coenzyme A, and vitamin B_1, and in glucosides, such as mustard oil and thiols which contribute the characteristic odor and taste to plants in

TABLE 2.13 Magnesium-Containing Carriers, Their Formula, Water Solubility, and Magnesium Content

Carrier	Formula	Water solubility	% Mg
Dolomitic limestone	$CaCO_3 + MgCO_3$	Insoluble	6–12
Kieseritie (magnesium sulfate)	$MgSO_4 \cdot H_2O$	Slightly	18
Epsom salt (magnesium sulfate)	$MgSO_4 \cdot 7H_2O$	Soluble	10
Potassium magnesium sulfate (SUL-PO-MG)	$K_2SO_4 \cdot MgSO_4$	Soluble	11
Pro/Mesium	$3MgO \cdot SiO_2 \cdot 2H_2O$	Insoluble	22
Magnesium oxide	MgO	Slightly	50–55

the Cruciferae and Liliaceae families. Sulfur also reduces the incidence of disease in many plants.

Content and Distribution in Plants—Sulfur content in leaf tissue ranges from 0.15 to 0.50% of the dry weight, total S content varying with plant species and stage of growth. The N to S ratio may be as important as total S alone or the ratio of sulfate-sulfur (SO_4-S) to total S as indicators of S sufficiency. Sufficiency ranges for a number of crops are given in Table 2.14.

Cruciferae accumulate three times as much S as P, Leguminosae accumulate equal amounts of S and P, while cereals accumulate one third less S than P.

Plants may contain from 10 to 80 lbs S/A (11 to 90 kg S/ha), with cereals, grasses, and potato removing approximately 10 lbs S/A, while sugar beet, cabbage, alfalfa, and cotton will remove from 15 to 40 lbs S/A (17 to 45 kg S/ha).

TABLE 2.14   Sufficiency Range for Sulfur in Selected Crops

Crop	Plant part	Sampling time	Sufficiency range (% S)
Field crops			
Alfalfa	Top 6 inches	First flower	0.25–0.50
Corn	Ear leaf	Initial silk	0.20–0.50
Peanut	Upper part of plant	Early pegging	0.20–0.30
Soybean	Most recent leaf	Prior to pod set	0.20–0.40
Vegetables			
Cucumber, field	5th leaf from top	Flower to small fruit set	0.30–1.00
Tomato, field	Adjacent top inflorescence	Mid-bloom	0.40–1.20
Fruits and nuts			
Apple	Mid-shoot current growth	Mid-season	0.20–0.40
Banana	6- to 9-month-old leaves		0.15–0.80
Orange	Behind fruit	5- to 7-month-old leaves	0.20–0.40
Pecan	Mid-portion terminal growth	56 to 84 days after terminal growth	0.20–0.50

Sulfur is synergistic with N and P, while an antagonistic relationship exists between S and arsenic (As), B, molybdenum (Mo), lead (Pb), selenium (Se), and Fe.

Available Forms for Root Absorption—Over 90% of available S exists in the soil organic matter, which has an approximate 10/1 nitrogen/sulfur (N/S) ratio. The sulfate (SO_4^{2-}) anion is the primary available form found in the soil solution. In general, most of the available SO_4 is found in the subsoil as the anion can be easily leached from the surface horizon. In addition, availability frequently depends on that deposited in rainfall (acid rain) and/or that released from organic matter decomposition.

At high soil pH (>7.0), S may be precipitated as calcium sulfate ($CaSO_4$), while at lower pH levels (<4.0), the SO_4^{2-} anion may be adsorbed by Al and Fe oxides.

Movement in Soil and Root Absorption—Sulfur moves in the soil as the SO_4^{2-} anion by mass flow and within the soil solution by diffusion. Therefore, low soil-moisture conditions can inhibit S uptake. Sulfate may precipitate as calcium sulfate ($CaSO_4$) around the roots if mass flow brings SO_4^{2-} anions at a rate greater than what can be absorbed.

Deficiency Symptoms—Plants deficient in S are light yellow-green in color initially over the entire plant, and fruits are light green and lack succulence. Roots are longer than normal and stems become woody; also root nodulation in legumes is reduced and delayed maturity occurs in grains. Interestingly, S deficiency is desired in tobacco in order to obtain proper leaf color.

Sulfur-deficiency symptoms can sometimes be confused with N-deficiency symptoms, although S symptoms normally affect the whole plant, while N deficiency symptoms occur initially on the older portions of the plant. Frequently on sandy and/or acid soils, symptoms of S deficiency may occur in newly emerging plants only to disappear as the plant roots enter the subsoil since S as SO_4^{2-} tends to accumulate in the subsoil under such soil conditions. Drought conditions may reduce the uptake of S, thereby inducing a S deficiency.

Excess (Toxicity) Symptoms—A premature senescence of leaves may occur.

TABLE 2.15   Sulfur-Containing Carriers, Their Formula, and Sulfur Content

Carrier	Formula	% S
Sulfur	S	90–100
Ammonium sulfate	$(NH_4)_2SO_4$	24
Gypsum	$CaSO_4 \cdot 2H_2O$	19
Magnesium sulfate (epsom salt)	$MgSO_4 \cdot 7H_2O$	13
Potassium sulfate	K_2SO_4	18
Potassium magnesium sulfate (SUL-PO-MAG)	$K_2SO_4 \cdot Mg_2SO_4$	23
Superphosphate	$CaSO_4$ + calcium phosphate	12
Ammonium thiosulfate	$(NH_4)_2S_2O_3$	26
Sulfur-coated urea	$CO(NH_2)_2\text{-}S$	10
Nitrogen-S solution	$CO(NH_2)_2 \cdot NH_4NO_3 \cdot (NH_4)_2SO_4$	2–5

Fertilizer Sources—Atmospheric deposition of S can occur downwind of large cities and industrial plants sufficient to meet S-crop requirements. However, S is becoming an increasingly occurring deficiency in many agricultural areas due to reduced atmospheric deposition and the use of low S-content fertilizers. Fertilizer sources for S are given in Table 2.15.

CHAPTER 3

The Micronutrients

Terminology

The seven micronutrients are boron (B), chlorine (Cl), copper (Cu), iron (Fe), manganese (Mn), molybdenum (Mo), and zinc (Zn), which have been variously identified in the past as either *trace or minor elements,* terms that are no longer used. The correct term is *micronutrient.*

The micronutrients are found and required in relatively low concentrations in plants compared to the major elements (see Table 1.2).

Micronutrient concentrations are expressed as parts per million (ppm) in this text, but as SI units, the terms would be either milligrams per kilogram (mg/kg) or millimole per kilogram (mmol/kg). Comparative values for the micronutrients in these three units are shown in this example (values were selected for illustrative purposes only):

Micronutrient	ppm	mg/kg	mmol/kg
Boron (B)	20	20	1.85
Chlorine (Cl)	100	100	2.82
Copper (Cu)	12	12	0.19
Iron (Fe)	111	111	1.98
Manganese (Mn)	55	55	1.00
Molybdenum (Mo)	1	1	0.01
Zinc (Zn)	33	33	0.50

TABLE 3.1 Approximate Concentration of the Micronutrients in Mature Leaf Tissue Generalized for Various Plant Species

| | Parts per million (ppm) | | |
Micronutrient	Deficient	Sufficient or normal	Excessive or toxic
Boron (B)	5–30	10–200	50–200
Chlorine (Cl)	100	100–500	500–1000
Cooper (Cu)	2–5	5–30	20–100
Iron (Fe)	<50	100–500	>500
Manganese (Mn)	15–25	20–300	300-500
Molybdenum (Mo)	0.03–0.15	0.1–2.0	>100
Zinc (Zn)	10–20	27–100	100–400

From Kabata-Pedias, A. and H. Pendias. 1994. *Trace Elements in Soils and Plants.* 2nd ed. CRC Press, Boca Raton, FL. With permission.

Content and Function

The approximate concentrations for the micronutrients in mature leaf tissue generalized for various plant species from deficient to sufficient or normal and to excessive or toxic are given in Table 3.1. Additional concentration

TABLE 3.2 Normal Range and Suggested Maximum Micronutrient Concentrations for Plant Leaves and Suggested Levels for Corn Leaves

| | Concentration of Metals in Plants (mg/kg, dry wt.) | | | |
| | Plant Leaves | | Corn Leaves | |
Element	Range	Maximum	Range	Maximum
Boron (B)	7–75	150	same	100
Copper (Cu)	3–40	150	5–25	30
Iron (Fe)	20–300	750	50–200	300
Manganese (Mn)	15–150	300	same	same
Molybdenum (Mo)	0.2–1.0	3	0.2–1.0	5[a]
Zinc (Zn)	15–150	300	20–100	300

[a] The level of Mo, which is toxic to cattle depends upon the concentration of Cu in rations. The recommended maximum could be toxic in very low Cu rations.
From Melsted, S.W. 1973. Soil-plant relationships (some practical considerations in waste management). In: *Proceedings Joint Conference on Recycling Municipal Sludges and Effluents on Land.* University of Illinois, Urbana.

TABLE 3.3   Sufficient Micronutrient Content of Plants at Feeks 718 Growth Stage

				mg/kg		
Crop	Boron (B)	Copper (Cu)	Iron (Fe)	Manganese (Mn)	Molybdenum (Mo)	Zinc (Zn)
Barley	5–10	5–10	21–200	25–150	0.10–0.3	15–60
Cotton	20–80	8–20	50–350	35–150	0.60–2.0	25–80
Groundnut	25–70	7–15	–	50–200	0.50–1.0	20–70
Maize	6–15	6–15	11–300	35–150	0.15–0.4	25–70
Oats	5–10	5–10	62–204	35–150	0.15–0.4	20–70
Potato	25–70	7–15	–	40–200	0.20–0.5	20–80
Rice	6–15	7–12	>80	40–150	0.40–1.0	30–70
Rye	4–10	5–10	–	20–100	0.10–0.3	15–60
Sorghum	5–15	5–12	50–250	25–150	0.15–0.3	15–60
Soybean	25–60	10–20	21–300	30–150	0.50–1.0	25–60
Sunflower	35–100	10–20	79–113	25–100	0.10–0.3	30–80
Wheat	5–10	5–10	21–200	35–150	0.10–0.3	20–70

Bergmann, W. 1983. *Ernähruggstörungen bei Kulturpflanzen, Entstehung und Diagnose.* Gustav Fischer Verlag, Jena , Germany.
Bergmann, W. and P. Neubert. 1976. *Pflanzendiagnose und Pflanzenanalyse.* Fischer, Jena, Germany.

range data are given in Tables 3.2 and 3.3. The fairly large sufficiency ranges shown in these tables are somewhat misleading because the concentration between deficiency and toxicity can be quite narrow for particular plant species as seen in the tables given with each micronutrient section in this text. The relative mass content for the seven micronutrients found in plants is given in Table 3.4, plus a brief description of their primary function in plants. More detailed information on function is given for each micronutrient in later in this text.

In general, the micronutrients Cl, Cu, Fe, and Mn are involved in various processes related to photosynthesis; therefore, their deficiency will be evident in terms of either significantly reduced plant growth and/or chlorosis symptoms. Four of the micronutrients, Cu, Fe, Mn, and Zn, are associated with various enzyme systems; Mo is specific for nitrate reductase only. Boron is the only micronutrient not specifically associated with either photosynthesis or enzyme function, but is associated with the carbohydrate chemistry and reproductive system of the plant.

TABLE 3.4 Micronutrient Essential for Growth and Their Average Content in Material from Cultivated Higher Plants and Approximate Concentration in the Environment

Micronutrient	Mass conc. (g/dry matter)	Molar conc. mmol (kg/dry matter)	No. of atoms relative to molybdenum	Conc. in environment (mol/m^3)	Examples of functions in cell
Chlorine (Cl)	0.1	3	3×10^3	0.001	Chloroplast photosystem II, metabolism, growth
Boron (B)	0.02	2	2×10^3	0.001	Carbohydrate chemistry, pollen germination and pollen tube development
Iron (Fe)	0.01	2	2×10^3	0.001	Energy transfer, proteins, co-enzyme factor prosthetic groups
Manganese (Mn)	0.05	1	1×10^3	0.001	Co-factor in water splitting enzyme, amino-peptidase, etc.
Zinc (Zn)	0.02	0.3	3×10^3	7×10^{-4}	Enzyme co-factor, carbonic anhydrase, alkaline phos-phatase, enzyme regulation
Copper (Cu)	0.06	0.3	1×10^3	3×10^{-4}	Constituent of plastocyanin, ascorbic acid, oxidase, etc.
Molybdenum (Mo)	0.0001	0.001	1	5×10^{-4}	Constituent of nitrate reductase

From Porter, J.R. and D.W. Lawlor, (eds.) 1991. *Plant Growth Interactions with Nutrition and Environment.* Society for Experimental Biology. Seminar Series 43. Cambridge University Press, New York, NY.

TABLE 3.5   Soil Conditions and Crops where Micronutrient Deficiencies Most Often Occur

Micronutrient	Sensitive crops	Soil conditions for deficiency
Boron (B)	alfalfa, clover, cotton, peanut, sugar beet, cabbage	acid sandy soils low in organic matter, overlimed soils, organic soils
Copper (Cu)	corn, onions, small grains, watermelon	organic soils, mineral soil high in pH and organic matter
Iron (Fe)	citrus, clover, pecan, sorghum, soybean	leached sandy soils low in organic matter, alkaline soils, soils high in phosphorus
Manganese (Mn)	alfalfa, small grains, soybean, sugar beet	leached acid soils, neutral to alkaline soil high in organic matter
Zinc (Zn)	corn, field beans, pecan, sorghum	leached acid sandy soils low in organic matter, neutral to alkaline soils and/or high in phosphorus

Soil and Plant Species Associations

The micronutrients are unique among the essential elements since their deficiency is frequently associated with a combination of crop species and soil characteristics. A list of some of the more common crop–soil associations is given in Table 3.5.

In addition, there are some crop plants that are uniquely sensitive to either deficiency or excess of a micronutrient (Table 3.6).

Boron

Functions in Plants—Boron is believed to be important in the synthesis of one of the bases for RNA (uracil) formation and in cellular activities (i.e., division, differentiation, maturation, respiration, growth, etc.). Boron has long been associated with pollen germination and growth and it improves

TABLE 3.6 Crop Species Sensitive to Either Deficient or Excessive Levels of the Micronutrients

Micronutrient	Sensitive to deficiency	Sensitive to excess
Boron (B)	Legumes, *Brassica* (cabbage and relatives), beets, celery, grapes, fruit trees (apple and pears), cotton, and sugar beet	Cereals, potato, tomato, cucumber, sunflower, and mustard
Chlorine (Cl)	Cereals, celery, potato, coconut palm, sugar beet, lettuce, carrot, and cabbage	Strawberry, navy bean, fruit trees, pea, and onion
Copper (Cu)	Cereals (oat), sunflower, spinach, alfalfa, onion, watermelon	Cereals and legumes, spinach, citrus seedlings, and gladiolus
Iron (Fe)	Fruit trees (citrus), grape, several calcifuge species, pecan, sorghum, soybean, and clover	Rice and tobacco
Manganese (Mn)	Cereals (oat), legumes, fruit trees (apple, cherries, and citrus), soybean, and sugar beet	Cereals, legumes, potato, and cabbage
Molybdenum (Mo)	*Brassica* (cabbage and relatives) and legumes	Cereals, pea, and green bean
Zinc (Zn)	Cereals (corn), legumes, grasses, hops, flax, grape, fruit trees (citrus), soybean, fieldbean, and pecan	Cereals and spinach

the stability of pollen tubes. Relatively immobile in plants, B is transported primarily in the xylem.

Content and Distribution in Plants—Based on their plant species, B requirements can be separated into three groups:

- Leaf content of monocots, 1 to 6 ppm B
- Dicots, 20 to 70 ppm B
- Dicots with latex system, 80 to 100 ppm B

Crop sensitivity to B varies with plant species as is shown in Table 3.7. The B sufficiency range for a number of crop species is given in Table 3.8.

TABLE 3.7 Relative Tolerance of Plants to Boron

Sensitive	Semi-tolerant	Tolerant
American elm, apple, apricot, avocado, blackberry, cherry, cowpea, elm, fig, grape, grapefruit, Jerusalem artichoke, kidney bean, kola, larkspur, lemon, lupine, navy bean, orange, pansy, peach, pear, pecan, persimmon, plum, strawberry, violet, walnut	Alfalfa, barley, birdsfoot trefoil, broccoli, calendula, California poppy, carrot, cauliflower, celery, clover, corn, field pea, hops, Kentucky bluegrass, lettuce, lima bean, millet, milo, mustard, oats, olive, onion, parsley parsnip, peanut, pepper, potato, pumpkin, radish, rice, rose, rutabaga, spinach, sunflower, sweet corn, sweet pea, sweet potato, timothy, tobacco, tomato, vetch, wheat, zinnia	Asparagus, artichoke, athel, blueberry, chard, cotton, cucumber, gladiolus, mangel, muskmelon, oxalis, palm, pasture grass, peppermint, rye, sesame, soybean, spearmint, sudangrass, sugar beet sweet clover, table beet, turnip

Boron tends to accumulate in leaf margins at concentrations five to ten times that found in the leaf blade (see Table 4.2). The level can become sufficiently high to result in marginal burning and death of the leaf margin.

A high calcium (Ca) content in the plant creates a high B requirement, while a high potassium (K) plant content accentuates the negative effect of low B tissue levels. Boron can exist in the plant as the borate (BO_3^{3-}) anion.

Available Forms for Root Absorption—Most of the B in soil exists in organic plant and microorganism residues. The release of B by residue decomposition is the major supply source for crop utilization. Boron exists in the soil solution as the borate (BO_3^{3-}) anion, although recent findings suggest that B can also exist as undissociated $B(OH)_3$. Since the major soil form is undissociated and is neutral in charge, the primary loss of B from soils is by leaching. Leaching is also a common technique of removing excess B from the surface soil and rooting zone.

Generally, total B in the soil can range from 20 to 200 ppm, while the amount available for plant absorption ranges from 1 to 5 ppm in the soil solution. The accepted range of B is narrow, with a deficiency occurring

TABLE 3.8.   Sufficiency Range for Boron in Selected Crops

Crop	Plant part	Sampling time	Sufficiency range (ppm B)
Field crops			
Alfalfa	Top 6 inches	First flower	30–80
Corn	Ear leaf	Initial silk	5–25
Peanut	Upper part of plant	Early pegging	20–50
Rice	Most recent leaf	Panicle initiation	6–7
Soybean	Most recent leaf	Prior to pod set	20–55
Vegetables			
Bean, snap	Upper developed leaves	Initial pod set	20–75
Cucumber, field	Fifth leaf from top	Flower to small fruit set	25–60
Lettuce, Cos type	Wrapper leaf	Mature	25–60
Potato, Irish	Upper developed leaf	30-cm tall	40–70
Tomato, field	Adjacent top inflorescence	Mid-bloom	25–60
Watermelon	Fifth leaf from top	Flower start, fruit set	25–60
Fruits and nuts			
Apple	Mid-shoot current growth	Mid-season	25–50
Banana	Six- to nine-month-old leaves		10–50
Grape	Petiole, opposite basal flower cluster	Full bloom	25–50
Olive	Mid-shoot		20–75
Orange	Behind fruit	Five- to seven-month-old leaves	25–100
Peach	Fruiting or non-fruiting spurs	Mid-summer	20–60
Pecan	Mid-portion terminal growth	56 to 84 days after terminal growth	15–50

when a hot water extract contains less than 1 ppm. Toxicity occurs at levels above 5 ppm.

Boron availability is also influenced by soil water pH; the optimum range for maximum availability lies between 5.5 to 7.0.

Movement in Soil and Root Absorption—Boron moves in soil by mass flow and diffusion, with B deficiency occurring when soil moisture levels are low for extended periods, or after a long period of heavy-leaching rainfall.

Deficiency Symptoms—Plants deficient in B exhibit an abnormal growth of growing points (meristematic tissue) with apical growing points eventually becoming stunted, and then die. Auxins accumulate at growing points, and leaves and stems become brittle.

TABLE 3.9 Micronutrient Containing Materials, Their Formula, and Micronutrient Content

Micronutrient sources	Formula	Micronutrient content (%)
Boron		
Fertilizer borate, 48	$Na_2B_4O_7 \cdot 10H_2O$	14–15
Fertilizer borate, granular	$Na_2B_4O_7 \cdot 10H_2O$	14
Foliarel	$Na_2B_8O_{13} \cdot 4H_2O$	21
Solubor	$Na_2B_4O_7 \cdot 4H_2O + Na_2B_{10}O_{16} \cdot 10H_2O$	20
Borax	$Na_2B_4O_7 \cdot 10H_2O$	11
Copper		
Copper sulfate (monohydrate)	$CuSO_4 \cdot H_2O$	35
Copper sulfate (pentahydrate)	$CuSO_4 \cdot 5H_2O$	25
Cupric oxide	CuO	75
Cuprous oxide	Cu_2O	89
Cupric ammonium phosphate	$CU(NH_4)PO_4 \cdot H_2O$	32
Basic copper sulfates	$CuSO_4 \cdot 3Cu(OH)_2$ (general formula)	13–53
Cupric chloride	$CuCl_2$	17
Copper chelates	$Na_2CuEDTA$	13
	$NaCuHEDTA$	9
Copper polyflavonoids	Organically bound Cu	5–7
Iron		
Ferrous ammonium phosphate	$Fe(NH_4)PO_4 \cdot H_2O$	29
Ferrous ammonium sulfate	$(NH_4)_2SO_4 \cdot FeSO_4 \cdot 6H_2O$	14
Ferrous sulfate	$FeSO_4 \cdot 7H_2O$	19–21
Ferric sulfate	$Fe(SO_4)_3 \cdot 4H_2O$	23
Iron chelates	$NaFeEDTA$	5–11
	$NaFeHFDTA$	5–9
	$NaFeEDDHA$	6
	$NaFeDTPA$	10
Iron polyflavonoids	Organically bound Fe	9–10
Manganese		
Manganese sulfate	$MnSO_4 \cdot 4H_2O$	26–28
Manganese oxide	MnO	41–68
Manganese chelate	Mn-EDTA	5–12

TABLE 3.9 Micronutrient Containing Materials, Their Formula, and Micronutrient Content (continued)

Micronutrient sources	Formula	Micronutrient content (%)
Molybdenum		
Ammonium molybdate	$(NH_4)_6MO_7O_{24} \cdot 2H_2O$	54
Sodium molybdate	$Na_2MoO_4 \cdot 2H_2O$	39–41
Molybdenum trioxide	MoO_3	66
Zinc		
Zinc sulfate	$ZnSO_4 \cdot H_2O$	35
Zinc oxide	ZnO	78–80
Zinc chelates	$Na_2ZnEDTA$	14
	NaZnTA	13
	NaZnHEDTA	9
Zinc polyflavonoids	Organically bound Zn	10

Excess (Toxicity) Symptoms—An excess of B causes leaf tips to become yellow, followed by necrosis. Leaves eventually assume a scorched appearance and prematurely fall off.

Fertilizer Sources—Boron can be either soil or foliar applied, rates of application ranging from 0.5 to 2.0 lbs B/A (0.56 to 2.2 kg B/ha) for soil application. Care is needed when applying since toxicity can occur from irregular soil distribution. A list of B fertilizer sources is given in Table 3.9.

Chlorine (Cl)

Functions in Plants—Chlorine is involved in the evolution of oxygen (O_2) in photosystem II in the photosynthetic process. Chlorine raises the cell osmotic pressure, affects stomatal regulation, and increases the hydration of plant tissue. Chlorine may be related to the suppression of leaf spot disease in wheat and fungus root disease in oat.

Content and Distribution in Plants—The leaf content of Cl ranges from low parts per million levels (20 ppm) in the dry matter to percent concentrations. A deficiency occurs in wheat when plant levels are less than 0.15%. Chlorine exists in the plant as the chloride (Cl^-) anion.

Available Forms for Root Absorption—Chlorine exists in the soil solution as the chloride (Cl^-) anion, which moves in the soil by mass flow. The Cl^- anion competes with other anions, such as nitrate (NO_3^-) and sulfate (SO_4^{2-}) for uptake.

Deficiency Symptoms—Typically, plants deficient in Cl exhibit a chlorosis of younger leaves and wilting of the plant. Deficiency is not common among most plants; however, for wheat and oats in some soil areas, Cl deficiency has been related to disease infestation.

Excess (Toxicity) Symptoms—An excess of Cl results in a premature yellowing of the leaves, burning of the leaf tips and margins, bronzing, and abscission of the leaves. Excess is primarily associated with salt-affected [high-sodium chloride (NaCl) content] soils, a condition which influences the osmotic characteristics of plant roots by restricting the uptake of water and other ions.

Fertilizer Sources—The use of chloride-containing fertilizers, such as potassium chloride (KCl), plus the trace amounts of Cl found in many fertilizer materials, would be sufficient in most cases to satisfy the crop requirement for Cl.

Copper (Cu)

Functions in Plants—Copper is a constituent of the chloroplast protein plastocyanin as well as serving as a part of the electron transport system linking photosystem I and II in the photosynthetic process. This element participates in protein and carbohydrate metabolism and nitrogen (N_2) fixation. It is a part of the enzymes that reduce both atoms of molecular oxygen (O_2) (cytochrome oxidase, ascorbic acid oxidase, and polyphenol oxidase). Also, Cu is involved in the desaturation and hydroxylation of fatty acids.

Content and Distribution in Plants—The Cu sufficiency range in leaves is between 3 to 7 ppm of the dry matter, while the toxicity range begins at

TABLE 3.10   Relative Tolerance of Plants to Copper

Low	Moderate	High
Asparagus, beans, *Lotus* spp., lupine, pasture grass, pea, peppermint, pine, potato, rape, rice, rye, rutabaga, soybean, spearmint	Apple, barley, broccoli, blueberry, cabbage, cauliflower, celery, corn, cotton, cucumber, mangel, parsnips, peach, pear, pineapple, pome and stone fruits, radish, sorghum, strawberry, sugar beets, sweet corn, Swiss chard, tomato, tung oil, turnip, vines	Alfalfa, barley, carrot, citrus, dill, lettuce, lucerne, millet, oat, onion, pangola grass, spinach, sudan-grass, sunflower, table beet, wheat

20 to 30 ppm. Much higher values, 20-200 ppm, can be tolerated if Cu has been applied as a fungicide.

In general, Cu deficiency is not likely to occur since the Cu requirement for most crops is quite low, unless the conditions given in Table 3.5 exist. The relative tolerance of crop plants to Cu is given in Table 3.10. Sufficiency ranges for a number of crop species are listed in Table 3.11.

Copper in the plant can interfere with Fe metabolism, which may result in the development of an Fe deficiency. In its interaction with Mo, Cu may interfere with the enzymatic reduction of nitrate (NO_3).

Available Forms for Root Absorption—Copper exists in the soil primarily in complexed form as low molecular weight organic compounds such as humic and fulvic acids. The cupric ion (Cu^{2+}) is present in very small quantities in the soil solution, with Cu deficiency occurring primarily on sandy and organic soils. Copper-uptake rates are lower than for most other micronutrients.

Movement in Soil and Root Absorption—Although the Cu supply in the soil solution is very low (<0.2 mg/kg) most soils have sufficient Cu to meet crop requirements. Most soils are able to maintain sufficient Cu^{2+} ions in the soil solution even with increasing soil pH. However with increasing organic matter content, Cu availability can be significantly reduced.

Deficiency Symptoms—Symptoms of Cu deficiency are reduced or stunted growth with distortion of young leaves and necrosis of the apical meristem. In trees, Cu deficiency may cause white tip or bleaching of younger leaves and summer dieback.

TABLE 3.11 Sufficiency Range for Copper in Selected Crops

Crop	Plant part	Sampling time	Sufficiency range (ppm Cu)
Field crops			
Alfalfa	Top 6 inches	First flower	7–30
Corn	Ear leaf	Initial silk	6–20
Peanut	Upper part of plant	Early pegging	10–50
Rice	Most recent leaf	Panicle initiation	8–25
Soybean	Most recent leaf	Prior to pod set	10–30
Winter wheat	Top two leaves	Just before heading	5–50
Vegetables			
Bean, snap	Upper developed leaves	Initial pod set	7–30
Cucumber, field	Fifth leaf from top	Flower to small fruit set	7–20
Lettuce, Cos type	Wrapper leaf	Mature	5–25
Potato, Irish	Upper developed leaf	30-cm tall	7–20
Tomato, field	Adjacent top inflorescence	Mid-bloom	5–20
Watermelon	Fifth leaf from top	Flower start, small fruit	6–20
Fruits and nuts			
Apple	Mid-shoot current growth	Mid-season	6–50
Banana	Six- to nine-month-old leaves		6–25
Orange	Behind fruit	Five- to seven-month-old leaves	6–100
Peach	Fruiting or non-fruiting spurs	Mid-summer	5–16
Pecan	Mid-portion terminal growth	56 to 84 days after terminal growth	6–30

Excess (Toxicity) Symptoms—An excess of Cu can induce Fe deficiency and chlorosis. Root growth may be suppressed, with inhibited elongation and lateral root formation at relatively low Cu levels in the soil solution. Copper is about 5 to 10 times more toxic to roots than Al and may more significantly affect root development into acid (pH <5.5) subsoils than Al.

Fertilizer Sources—Copper can be either soil or foliar applied, with Cu sources given in Table 3.9.

Iron

Functions in Plant—Iron is an important component in many plant enzyme systems, such as cytochrome oxidase (electron transport) and cytochrome (terminal respiration step). Iron is a component of protein ferredoxin and is required for nitrate (NO_3) and sulfate (SO_4) reduction, nitrogen (N_2) assimilation, and energy (NADP) production. It functions as a catalyst or part of an enzyme system associated with chlorophyll formation. It is thought that Fe is involved in protein synthesis and root-tip meristem growth. The plant and soil chemistry of Fe is highly complex with both aspects still under intensive study.

Content and Distribution in Plants—Leaf Fe content ranges from 10 to 1,000 ppm in the dry matter with sufficiency ranging from 50 to 75 ppm, although total Fe may not always be related to sufficiency. In general, 50 ppm Fe is the generally accepted critical value for most crops with deficiency likely when total leaf Fe is less. An accurate determination of Fe plant content is normally not possible since extraneous sources of Fe are difficult to exclude from the determination, soil and dust contamination being the primary contributor to extraneous Fe.

Iron deficiency affects many crops, a common deficiency occurring on alkaline soils, and frequently referred to as *lime chlorosis*. A list of ornamental plants intolerant to high-lime soils is given in Table 3.12.

TABLE 3.12 Ornamental Plants Intolerant to High-Lime Soils

Groundcovers	Shrubs and trees	Other herbaceous plants
Dichondra, strawberry, spring cinquefoil, African daisy, star daisy, periwinkle, and many turf species	Abelia, acacia, azalea, bottle brush, camellia, catalpa, citrus, eucalyptus, hibiscus, hydrangea, walnut, sweet gum, crabapple, photina, Monterey pine, evergreen pear, firethorn, rhododendron, rose, weeping willow, Western red cedar, viburnum, wisteria, peach, gardenia, raspberry, juniper, spirea, privet, lilac, honey-suckle, tea tree, avocado, magnolia, pin oak, heavenly bamboo	Petunia, peony, iris, gladiolus, geranium, lupine, verbena, ferns

The majority of plant Fe is in the ferric (Fe^{3+}) form as ferric phosphoprotein, although the ferrous (Fe^{2+}) ion is believed to be the metabolically active form.

High phosphorus (P) decreases the solubility of Fe in the plant, a P:Fe ratio of 29:1 being average for most plants. Potassium increases the mobility and solubility of Fe, while nitrogen (N) accentuates Fe deficiency due to increased growth. The bicarbonate (HCO_3^-) anion is believed to interfere with Fe uptake and translocation within the plant. High zinc (Zn) can interfere with Fe metabolism resulting in a visual symptom of Fe deficiency.

Extractable ferrous (Fe^{2+}) iron may be a better indicator of plant-Fe status than total Fe. Various extraction procedures have been proposed for diagnosing Fe deficiency, with 20 to 25 ppm as being the critical extractable-Fe range.

However, most methods of determining the Fe status of the plant by means of an Fe analysis, whether total or extractable, are flawed (from the presence of soil and dust particles on tissue as well as Fe added in plant tissue processing) and pose a difficult problem for correctly assessing the Fe status of a plant. The indirect measurement of chlorophyll content may be the best alternative method for Fe-sufficiency diagnosis.

Available Forms for Root Absorption—Iron exists in the soil as both the ferric (Fe^{3+}) and ferrous (Fe^{2+}) cations. The Fe^{2+} form, whose availability is affected by the degree of soil aeration, is thought to be the active form taken up by plants. Iron-sufficient plants are able to acidify the rhizosphere as well as release Fe-complexing substances, such as siderophores, which enhance Fe availability and uptake, while Fe-inefficient plants do not exhibit similar root characteristics. A list of Fe-sensitive crops are given in Table 3.13.

Movement in Soil and Root Absorption—Iron moves in the soil by mass

TABLE 3.13 Iron-Sensitive Crops

Fruit and nut crops	*Others*
Apple, apricot, avocado, banana, blueberry, brambles, cacao, cherry, citrus, coconut, coffee, grape, nuts (almond, filbert, pecan, walnut), olive, peach, pear, pineapple, plum, strawberry, tung	Corn, rice, sorghum, soybean, sugarcane

flow and diffusion, and when an Fe ion reaches the rhizosphere, it will be reduced (from Fe^{3+} to Fe^{2+}), or be released from a chelated form (although chelated Fe can also be taken into the plant as the chelate), and then absorbed. Copper, manganese (Mn), and calcium (Ca) competitively inhibit Fe uptake, and high levels of phosphorus (P) will also reduce Fe uptake.

Deficiency Symptoms—Interveinal chlorosis of younger leaves is the typical symptom of deficiency, and as the severity of the deficiency increases, chlorosis spreads to the older leaves.

Excess (Toxicity) Symptoms—Iron may accumulate to several hundred ppm without toxicity symptoms. When at a toxic level (not clearly defined), a bronzing of the leaves with tiny brown spots on the leaves will appear, a typical symptom frequently occurring with rice.

Fertilizer Sources—Iron sources can be either soil or foliar applied, with foliar application being the most efficient using either a solution of ferrous sulfate ($FeSO_4$) or one of the chelated (EDTA or EDDHA) forms of Fe. A list of Fe sources is given in Table 3.9.

Manganese

Functions in Plants—Manganese is involved in the oxidation-reduction processes in the photosynthetic electron transport system. It is essential in the photosystem II for photolysis, acts as a bridge for ATP and enzyme complex phosphokinase and phosphotransferases, and activates IAA oxi-

TABLE 3.14   Relative Sensitivity of Plants to Manganese

Low sensitivity	Moderate sensitivity	High sensitivity
Asparagus, blueberry, cotton, rye	Alfalfa, barley, broccoli, cabbage, carrot, cauliflower, celery, clover, cucumber, corn, grass, parsnips, peppermint, sorghum, spearmint, sugar beet, tomato, turnip	Beans, citrus, lettuce, oats onion, pea, peach, potato, radish, soybean, spinach, sudangrass, table beet, wheat

TABLE 3.15 Sufficiency Range for Manganese (Mn) in Selected Crops

Crop	Plant part	Sampling time	Sufficiency range (ppm Mn)
Field crops			
Alfalfa	Top 6 inches	First flower	30–100
Corn	Ear leaf	Initial silk	20–200
Peanut	Upper part of plant	Early pegging	100–350
Rice	Most recent leaf	Panicle initiation	150–800
Soybean	Most recent leaf	Prior to pod set	20–100
Winter wheat	Top two leaves	Just before heading	16–200
Vegetables			
Bean, snap	Upper developed leaves	Initial pod set	50–300
Cucumber, field	Fifth leaf from top	Flower to small fruit set	50–300
Lettuce, Cos type	Wrapper leaf	Mature	11–250
Potato, Irish	Upper developed leaf	30-cm tall	30–250
Tomato, field	Adjacent top inflorescence	Mid-bloom	40–250
Watermelon	Fifth leaf from top	Flower start, small fruit	50–250
Fruits and nuts			
Apple	Mid-shoot current growth	Mid-season	25–200
Banana	Six- to nine-month-old leaves		100–1000
Grape	Petiole, opposite basal flower cluster	Full bloom	18–100
Olive	Mid-shoot		25+
Orange	Behind fruit	Five- to seven-month-old leaves	25–200
Peach	Fruiting or non-fruiting spurs	Mid-summer	40–160
Pecan	Mid-portion terminal growth	56 to 84 days after terminal growth	200–500

dases.

Content and Distribution in Plants—The leaf sufficiency content of Mn ranges from 10 to 50 ppm in the dry matter in mature leaves. Tissue levels will reach 200 ppm or higher (soybean, 600 ppm; cotton, 700 ppm; sweet potato, 1380 ppm) before severe toxicity symptoms develop. The relative sensitivity to Mn by crop species is given in Table 3.14, while the sufficiency range by crop species is given in Table 3.15.

Manganese is not known to interfere with the metabolism or uptake of any of the other essential elements.

Available Forms for Roots Absorption—Manganese exists in the soil solution as either Mn^{2+}, Mn^{3+}, and Mn^{4+} cations and as exchangeable Mn. The cation Mn^{2+} is the ionic form taken up by plants. Availability is significantly affected by soil pH, decreasing when the pH increases above 6.2 in some soils, while in other soils, the decrease may not occur until the soil water pH reaches 7.5. Manganese availability can be reduced significantly by low soil temperatures. In addition, soil organic matter can have an effect on Mn availability, decreasing its availability with an increase in organic matter content.

Movement in Soil and Root Absorption—Manganese is primarily supplied to the plant by mass flow and root interception. Low soil temperature and moisture stress will reduce Mn uptake. Some plants may release root exudates that reduce Mn^{4+} to Mn^{2+}, complex it, thereby increasing Mn availability to the plant.

Deficiency Symptoms—For dicots, reduced or stunted growth with visual interveinal chlorosis on the younger leaves is symptomatic of Mn deficiency. Cereals develop gray spots on their lower leaves (*grey speck*), and legumes develop necrotic areas on their cotyledons (*marsh spot*).

Excess (Toxicity) Symptoms—Symptoms of an excess of Mn is seen on the older leaves as brown spots surrounded by a chlorotic zone or circle. Black specks on stone fruits, particularly for apple, and similar black specks on young bark, referred to as *measles,* is the visual evidence of high Mn content in the tissue.

Fertilizer Sources—Manganese is best applied as a foliar spray to correct a deficiency as soil applications can be very inefficient due to soil inactivation of applied Mn. Row application of a phosporus (P) fertilizer will increase Mn availability and uptake. A list of Mn sources is given in Table 3.9.

Molybdenum

Functions in Plant—Molybdenum is a component of two major enzyme systems, nitrogenase and nitrate reductase. Nitrogenase is involved in the conversion of nitrate (NO_3) to the ammonium (NH_4). Therefore, the requirement for Mo is reduced greatly if the primary form of nitrogen (N) available to the plant is NH_4.

Content and Distribution—The leaf content of Mo is usually less than 1 ppm in the dry matter, due in part to the very low level of the molybdate (MnO_4^{2-}) anion in the soil solution.

Molybdenum can be taken up in higher amounts without resulting in toxic effects to the plant. However, high Mo content (>10 ppm Mo) forage can pose a serious health hazard to cattle, particularly dairy cows which have a sensitive copper (Cu) to Mo balance requirement. The normal Mo plant content ranges from 0.34 to 1.5 ppm.

Available Forms for Root Absorption—The primary soluble soil form is the molybdate (MoO_4^{2-}) anion, whose availability is increased 10-fold for each unit increase in soil pH. In the soil, Mo is strongly absorbed by Fe and Al oxides whose formation is pH dependent.

Movement in Soil and Root Absorption—Mass flow and diffusion equally supply Mo to roots, although mass flow supplies most of the Mo when the soil Mo level is high.

If nitrate (NO_3) is the primary N source, Mo uptake is higher than if ammonium (NH_4) is equal to or greater than NO_3 as the source of N. In general, P and Mg will enhance Mo uptake, while sulfate (SO_4) will reduce uptake.

Deficiency Symptoms—Molybdenum deficiency symptoms frequently resemble N deficiency symptoms. Older and middle leaves become chlorotic first, and in some instances, leaf margins are rolled and growth and flower formation is restricted. Cruciferae and pulse crops have high Mo requirements (see Table 3.6). In cauliflower, the middle lamella of the cell wall is not formed completely when Mo is deficient, with only the leaf rib formed, thereby giving a *whip-tail* appearance in severe cases. *Whip-tail* is a commonly used term to describe a Mo deficiency.

Excess (Toxicity) Symptoms—High plant Mo does not normally affect the plant, but can pose a problem for ruminant animals, particularly dairy cows, that consume plants containing 5 ppm or more Mo.

Fertilizer Sources—Molybdenum is best supplied by means of seed treatment, the sources of Mo given in Table 3.9.

Zinc

Functions in Plants—Zinc is involved in the same enzymatic functions as are manganese (Mn) and magnesium (Mg) with only carbonic anhydrase being activated by Zn.

Content and Distribution—In general, the leaf sufficiency range for Zn is from 15 to 50 ppm in the dry matter in mature leaves, but for some species, visual deficiency symptoms will not appear until the Zn content is as low as 12 ppm. For the majority of crops, 15 ppm Zn in the leaves is considered the *critical value*. However, a small variation in Zn content, as little as 1 to 2 ppm at the critical level, may be sufficient to establish either deficiency or sufficiency. Some plants can accumulate considerable quantities of Zn (several 100 ppm) without harm to the plant. A list of the sufficiency range for a number of crops is given in Table 3.16.

The relationship between phosphorus (P) and Zn has been intensively studied as research suggests that high P can interfere with Zn metabolism as well as affect the uptake of Zn through the root. High Zn can induce an iron (Fe) deficiency, particularly those sensitive to Fe (see Table 3.13).

Available Forms for Root Absorption—Zinc exists in the soil solution as the Zn^{2+} cation, as exchangeable Zn, and as organically complexed Zn. Availability is affected by soil pH, decreasing with increasing pH. Zinc availability can also be reduced when the available soil P level is very high.

Movement in Soil and Root Absorption—Zinc is brought into contact with plant roots by mass flow and diffusion, with diffusion being the primary delivery mechanism. Copper (Cu^{2+}) and other cations, such as ammonium (NH_4^+), will inhibit root Zn uptake. Phosphorus appears to inhibit translocation rather than directly inhibiting uptake.

TABLE 3.16 Sufficiency Range for Zinc in Selected Crops

Crop	Plant part	Sampling time	Sufficiency range (ppm Zn)
Field crops			
Alfalfa	Top 6 inches	First flower	20–70
Corn	Ear leaf	Initial silk	25–100
Peanut	Upper part of plant	Early pegging	20–50
Rice	Most recent leaf	Panicle initiation	18–50
Soybean	Most recent leaf	Prior to pod set	20–50
Winter wheat	Top two leaves	Just before heading	20–70
Vegetables			
Bean, snap	Upper developed leaves	Initial pod set	20–200
Cucumber, field	Fifth leaf from top	Flower to small fruit set	25–100
Lettuce, Cos type	Wrapper leaf	Mature	20–250
Potato, Irish	Upper developed leaf	30-cm tall	30–200
Tomato, field	Adjacent top inflorescence	Mid-bloom	20–50
Watermelon	Fifth leaf from top	Flower start, small fruit	20–50
Fruits and nuts			
Apple	Mid-shoot current growth	Mid-season	20–100
Banana	Six- to nine-month-old leaves		20–200
Grape	Petiole, opposite basal flower cluster	Full bloom	20–30
Olive	Mid-shoot		25+
Orange	Behind fruit	Five- to seven-month-old leaves	25–200
Peach	Fruiting or non-fruiting spurs	Mid-summer	20–50
Pecan	Mid-portion terminal growth	56 to 84 days after terminal growth	50–100

The efficiency of Zn uptake seems to be enhanced by a reduction in pH of the rhizosphere, with those plant species that can readily reduce the pH being less affected by low soil Zn than those that cannot.

Deficiency Symptoms—Zinc deficiency appears as a chlorosis in the interveinal areas of new leaves, producing a banding appearance. With increasing severity of the deficiency, leaf and plant growth become stunted (rosette), and leaves die and fall off the plant. At branch terminals of fruit and nut trees, rosetting occurs with considerable die back of the branches.

Excess (Toxicity) Symptoms—Plants particularly sensitive to Fe (see Table 3.10) will become chlorotic when Zn levels are abnormally high (>100 ppm). However, there are some plant species that can tolerate relatively high Zn contents (100 to 250 ppm) without a significant affect on plant growth and yield.

Fertilizer Sources—Zinc can be applied to the plant by means of both soil and foliar applications, a list of Zn sources given in Table 3.9.

CHAPTER 4

Plant Analysis

Purpose

Plant analysis, sometimes referred to as leaf analysis, is a technique that determines the elemental content of a particular plant part. Normally, plant analysis refers to a laboratory analysis of collected plant tissue. By contrast, tissue testing—an analysis of extracted cellular sap—is normally carried out in the field, making use of specially prepared papers and reagents in a designed testing kit. Tissue testing is discussed in the next chapter.

Using established *critical* or *standard values*, or *sufficiency ranges*, a comparison is made between the laboratory analysis result with one or more of these known values or ranges in order to access the plant's nutritional status.

Another system of plant analysis interpretation is called DRIS, the acronym for *Diagnosis and Recommendation Integrated System*, a method of using ratios of elemental contents to establish a series of values that will identify those elements from the most to the least deficient. These various methods of plant analysis interpretation will be discussed later in this chapter.

Plant analysis, as a diagnostic technique, has a considerable history of application. More recently, plant analysis results are being used to determine the combined soil and crop nutrient element status from which a prescribed lime and fertilizer recommendation can be made. Using a sequence of plant analyses to track or log changes in nutrient element status during the growing season, growers can determine when supplemental fertilizer treatments are needed.

A number of objectives in utilizing a plant analysis result have been proposed, most frequently:

- Verification of deficiency symptoms
- Evaluation of the nutritional status of the soil/crop environment
- Determination of nutrient element needs for the sampled and/or future crop
- Crop logging

Most importantly, plant analysis findings are used to determine if the soil fertility level and applied fertilizers were sufficient to meet the crop requirement for the essential elements. This latter application—probably the most important use of a plant analysis finding—is the least understood and used.

Sequence of Procedures

A plant analysis is carried out as a series of steps:

- Sampling
- Sample preparation
- Laboratory analysis
- Interpretation

Each step in the sequence is equally important to the success of the technique. A diagram of this sequence is given in Figure 4.1.

Sampling Techniques

Since plant species, age, plant part, and time sampled are variables that affect the interpretation of a plant analysis result, careful sampling is important. In addition, most of the essential elements are not equally distributed in the plant or within its parts.

Procedures for collecting a plant tissue sample for either field or laboratory determination of its elemental content have been widely published. A brief listing of sampling procedures for some common crops and plants are given in Table 4.1.

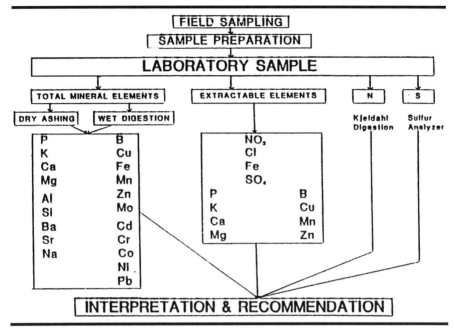

FIGURE 4.1 Sequence of procedures for conducting a plant analysis.

The important components for proper plant tissue collection are:

- Definite plant part taken at a specific location on the plant
- Stage of plant growth or specific time of sampling
- Number of parts taken per plant
- Number of plants selected for sampling

Following the sampling directions prescribed, the sampler should achieve reasonable statistical reliability.

Sampling instructions are quite specific in terms of plant part and stage of growth (see Table 4.1), since a comparison of an assay result with established critical or standard values, or sufficiency ranges, are based on a clearly identified plant part taken at a specified time. Sufficiency ranges are given for a number of crops in Chapter 2 for the major elements and Chapter 3 for the micronutrients. It should be emphasized that an analysis of a different plant part or a plant part taken at a time other than that specified may not be interpreted easily using established interpretative data.

When no specific sampling instructions are given or are unknown, the general rule of thumb is to select upper mature leaves.

TABLE 4.1 Sampling Procedures for Selected Crops for Conducting a Plant Analysis

Crop	Plant part	Sampling time	Number Leaves	Number Plants
Field crops				
Alfalfa	Top 6 inches	First flower	12	12
Corn	Ear leaf	Initial silk	15	15
Peanut	Upper part of plant	Early pegging	25	25
Rice	Most recent leaf	Panicle initiation	25	25
Soybean	Most recent leaf	Prior to pod set	50	25
Winter wheat	Top two leaves	Just before heading	50	50
Vegetables				
Bean, snap	Upper developed leaves	Initial pod set	30	15
Cucumber, field	Fifth leaf from top	Flower to small fruit set	24	12
Lettuce, Cos type	Wrapper leaf	Mature	12	12
Potato, Irish	Upper developed leaf	30-cm tall	50	25
Tomato, field	Adjacent top inflorescence	Mid-bloom	30	15
Watermelon	Fifth leaf from top	Flower start, small fruit	24	12
Fruits and nuts				
Apple	Mid-shoot current growth	Mid-season	50	25
Banana	Six- to nine-month-old leaves		15	15
Grape	Petiole, opposite basal flower cluster	Full bloom	30	15
Olive	Mid-shoot		50	25
Orange	Behind fruit	Five- to seven-month-old leaves	30	15
Peach	Fruiting or non-fruiting spurs	Mid-summer	30	15
Pecan	Mid-portion terminal growth	56 to 84 days after terminal growth	50	25

What Not to Sample

Avoidance criteria are also crucial. Plants to be avoided are ones that:

- Have been under long climatic or nutritional stress
- Have been damaged mechanically or by insects

- Are infested with disease
- Are covered with dust or soil, or foliar-applied spray materials unless these extraneous substances can be removed effectively (decontamination procedures are discussed later in this chapter)
- Are border row plants or shaded leaves within the plant canopy
- Contain dead plant tissue

Number of Plants to Sample

Precision requirements will dictate the number of plant parts to be collected and what number of plants to sample in order to make a composite sample, or just how many composite samples will be necessary to ensure sufficient replication. Various studies indicate that the number of individual leaves and/or plants required is correlated with the desired variance to be obtained, as is illustrated in Figure 4.2.

In addition, sampling requirements are considerably more complex when plants are under stress due to the high variability in plant characteristics as a result of such conditions. Therefore, in order to achieve statistical verification, a more intensive sampling routine may be required.

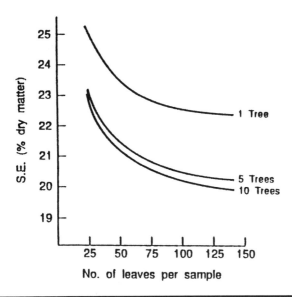

FIGURE 4.2 Variance associated with the number of leaves sampled per tree.

In the example shown in Figure 4.2, the variance was more significantly affected by the number of trees sampled rather than by the number of leaves sampled per tree. The combination of the number of plants selected for sampling plus the number of samples per plant determines the variance associated with the final analysis result.

Normally, the mean value of several composite sample assays is a more accurate estimate than a single assay result based on a single composite sample consisting of the same total number of individual samples.

Lack of Homogeneity

How a plant tissue sample is selected is important because the distribution of the essential elements within the plant, and even within any one of its parts, is not homogeneous due to a number of factors. For example, as plant tissues mature, there are changes due to:

- The movement of mobile elements from the older tissue to newly developing tissues
- An accumulation of non-mobile elements
- A reduction in dry matter content

One sign of increasing maturity in leaves is an increasing concentration (accumulation) of calcium (Ca) and magnesium (Mg), and a decreasing concentration (reduction) of nitrogen (N) phosphorus (P), and potassium (K).

Another factor contributing to the variation is the relative proportion of leaf blade to mid-rib and the size of the leaf, anatomical factors that can affect the concentration of elements found in the whole leaf. For example, the leaf mid-rib will normally contain a higher concentration of K than the blade. Similarly, the relative proportion of leaf blade to margin affects the boron (B) and manganese (Mn) contents of the whole leaf since these two elements accumulate to fairly high concentrations in the leaf margin.

A sampling procedure that would enhance the distribution effect of elements within the leaf will affect the analysis result. For instance, a sampling procedure in which only the leaf tips are sampled or blade punches are collected, will produce a different analytical result compared to the assay of the entire intact leaf. The effect of dividing a corn leaf into four equal sections on elemental concentration is shown in Table 4.2.

TABLE 4.2   Element Content of a Whole Corn Ear Leaf and Four Equal-Length Sections

Element	Whole leaf	Equal quarter-length sections of the ear leaf (%)			
		Tip	Upper middle	Lower middle	Base
		%			
Nitrogen (N)	2.93	3.20	3.65	2.75	1.95
Phosphorus (P)	0.22	0.22	0.23	0.25	0.18
Potassium (K)	1.22	1.26	1.19	1.44	1.23
Calcium (Ca)	0.48	0.75	0.58	0.48	0.35
Magnesium (Mg)	0.39	0.40	0.41	0.45	0.40
		ppm			
Boron (B)	11	25	14	8	6
Copper (Cu)	9	12	10	10	8
Iron (Fe)	96	110	102	75	57
Manganese (Mn)	73	124	79	62	49
Zinc (Zn)	22	30	22	22	18

From Jones, J.B., Jr. 1970. Distribution of fifteen elements in corn leaves, *Commun. Soil Sci. Plant Anal.*: 1:27–33.

Petioles

Petioles are not a part of the leaf blade and should not be included in a leaf sample. For some crops, such as grape and sugar beet, the petiole may be the plant part to be assayed rather than the leaf blade. Petioles, being conductive tissue, are higher in certain elements, such as K, P, and nitrate-nitrogen (NO_3-N), than the attached leaf blade

Comparative Samples

Sampling two different populations of plants for comparative purposes can also be difficult, particularly when some type of stress has resulted in substantial differences in growth characteristics. When two or more sets of plants exhibit varying signs of a possible nutrient element insufficiency, collecting tissue for comparative purposes is desirable, but it can be difficult due in part to the effect of the nutrient element stress on plant growth and development. It is important, whenever possible, to obtain plant tissue samples when the symptoms of stress first appear. Therefore, great care must be taken to ensure that representative samples are collected for such comparisons, and that the interpretation of the analysis result takes into consideration the condition of the plants when they were sampled, whether normal in physical appearance or not, due to some type of stress.

Inappropriate Plant Tissue

Although it is possible to assay just about any plant part, or even the whole plant itself, the biological significance of an analysis result is dependent on the availability of interpretative data for the plant part collected and assayed.

For example, the assay of fruits and grain, or an analysis of the whole plant or one of its parts at maturity or at harvest, does not usually provide reliable information on the nutritional status of the plant during its earlier growth period.

When conducting a plant analysis, the primary objective should be to obtain that plant part for which assay results can be compared to known interpretative values.

Plant Tissue Preparation

Decontamination

Decontamination to remove foreign substances from the surface of tissue may be necessary, particularly if they contain elements that are essential for the interpretation of the analysis result. Normally, decontamination is required when plants are covered with soil and dust particles, or the foliage is coated with foliar-applied materials that contain elements of interest in the plant analysis determination. If iron (Fe) is an element of primary interest, plant tissue must be decontaminated; otherwise, the Fe analysis result will be highly suspect. In general, if Fe is not an element of primary interest, rainfall or the application of overhead irrigation will normally keep just-maturing leaf tissue relatively free from a significant accumulation of dust and soil particles; therefore, decontamination may not be necessary. However, if plants are not regularly bathed with either rainfall or overhead irrigation, dust and soil particles will begin to accumulate on leaf tissue;

decontamination to remove these accumulated particles may be necessary. Only fresh, fully turgid plant tissue can be subjected to a decontamination procedure.

The characteristics of the tissue surface will determine the effectiveness of the decontamination process. Rough surfaced tissue or tissue that has a pubescent surface may be impossible to decontaminate.

In some instances, the decontamination procedure itself may significantly alter the elemental composition of the tissue. The procedure may add elements to the tissue, or it may leach elements from it, such as potassium (K) and boron (B).

Decontamination Procedure

The most effective decontamination procedure is to wash—quickly (20 to 30 seconds)—fresh, fully turgid tissue in a mild 2% phosphorus-free detergent solution, one leaf at a time, rubbing the tissue surface gently with the fingers. The detergent solution is then quickly washed from the tissue surface with flowing pure water. The plant material is shaken to remove the excess water and then oven-dried at 176°F (80°C).

Dry Weight Preservation

It should be remembered that elemental concentration is based on the dry weight of tissue; therefore, any condition that affects the dry weight of collected plant tissue will affect its elemental composition.

If collected plant tissue begins to decay, significant reductions in dry weight can occur as well as the loss by volatilization of some elements, particularly nitrogen (N) and sulfur (S).

Fresh plant tissue should not be placed in plastic bags unless the temperature is kept below 40°F (5°C). Air drying tissue prior to shipment to the plant analysis laboratory will minimize the loss in dry weight. If at all possible, plant tissue should be delivered to the laboratory within 24 hours of collection, irrespective of the method used to control the loss of dry weight.

Contamination

Maintaining the integrity of the collected sample is also crucial in order to ensure accurate assay results. When collecting plant tissue, care should be taken to ensure that the sample is not altered chemically, or contaminated by extraneous materials as a result of contact with sampling tools and containers.

For example, if the particle size reduction device has brass fittings, copper (Cu) and zinc (Zn) will be added to the sample; if the device is made of tool or stainless steel, Fe will be added to the sample. The extent of these additions will depend on the length of contact time and the physical condition of the milling device.

Oven drying at 176°F (80°C) and sample size reduction (milling) prepares the sample for laboratory analysis. Then the organic matter in the tissue must be destroyed by either wet acid oxidation or high temperature dry ashing in order to bring the elements into suitable form for analysis.

Laboratory Analysis

A number of different analytical procedures is required to assay for all of the essential elements. Procedures in common use in plant analysis laboratories include:

- Kjeldahl digestion or dry combustion for nitrogen (N)
- Dry combustion of sulfur (S)
- Colorimetry for boron (B), phosphorus (P), and molybdenum (Mo)
- Flame emission spectrophotometry for potassium (K) and sodium (Na)
- Flame atomic absorption spectrometry for calcium (Ca), copper (Cu), iron (Fe), magnesium (Mg), maganese (Mn), and zinc (Zn)
- Flameless atomic absorption spectrometry for molybdenum (Mo)
- Specific-ion electrodes or ion chromatography for the determination of chloride (Cl), sulfate (SO_4), and nitrate (NO_3) anions

More recently, inductively coupled plasma emission spectrometry, frequently known by its acronym ICP or ICAP, has become the analytical procedure of choice since most of the elements that could be determined by either spectrophotometry (colorimetry) and flame emission or atomic absorption spectrophotometry are easily assayed by the ICP technique simultaneously. Laboratories using this analytical methodology are able to provide rapid, low-cost analytical service, making a plant analysis determination cost effective and an extremely valuable tool for ensuring plant nutrient element sufficiency.

Methods of Interpretation

Difficulties have been encountered in the use and interpretation of plant analyses, even though the quantitative association between an absorbed essential element and plant growth has been widely studied. Questions raised at the 1959 Plant Analysis and Fertilizer Problems Colloquium regarding the limitations of the plant analysis technique are still applicable today:

- The reliability of interpretative data
- The utilization of ratio and balance concepts
- Hybrid influences
- Changing physiological processes that occur at varying elemental concentrations

Today, reliable interpretative data is still lacking for:

- The micronutrient Cl
- Most of the essential elements for ornamental plants
- Most plants during their very early stages of growth
- Identification of elemental concentrations considered excessive or toxic

It is also questionable whether the determination of the Fe concentration in a particular plant tissue can be used to establish the degree of Fe sufficiency due to the problem of contamination and the characteristics of Fe within the plant itself (see Chapter 3).

Initially, single concentration values, such as critical or standard values or concentrations, were sought. But today, those who interpret plant analysis results for diagnostic purposes want values that list the full concentration range from deficiency to excess. Such interpretative data have been obtained from response curves, as illustrated in Figure 4.3, data that have and continue to be gathered from continuing research studies and the gathering of analytical data from production fields. Other analysts have drawn similar response curves with varying slopes within the deficiency range, as shown in Figure 4.4.

The slope and general configuration shown in Figure 4.3 describe the typical association between yield or plant response and the macronutrient concentration in the leaf or plant. Figure 4.4 better typifies the association between yield and a micronutrient concentration.

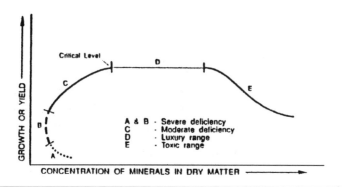

FIGURE 4.3   General relationship between plant growth to yield and elemental content of the plant (Smith, 1962; with permission).

The C-shape of the left-hand portion of Figure 4.3 has been termed the Steenbjerg effect. This phenomenon results from the combination of elemental accumulation and dry matter reduction that frequently occurs when plants are under stress. If the interpreter is not familiar with this interactive relationship—element concentration and dry matter accumulation or reduction—a misinterpretation of the plant analysis may result.

The steep left-hand slope in Figure 4.4 poses a significant sampling and analytical problem since this response curve indicates that a very small change in concentration results in a significant change in plant growth and/ or yield. This phenomenon is primarily associated with the micronutrients, such as Mn and Zn, where a relatively small change in concentration—a

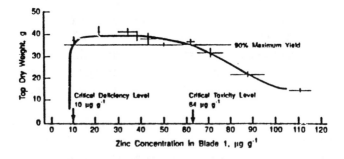

FIGURE 4.4   Relationship between zinc content on blade 1 of grain sorghum and top dry weight (Okhi, 1987; with permission).

change of 1 or 2 ppm in the leaf tissue—can define the difference between deficiency or sufficiency of these elements.

In an ever-increasing number of instances, identifying an excessive or toxic concentration level for an essential element has become as important as that for identifying the level that would be considered deficient. Unfortunately, very little information exists that defines the full range of response from deficiency to toxicity.

Critical Values

A critical value is the concentration below which deficiency occurs. This single value is difficult to use when a plant analysis result is considerably above or below the critical value. Some authorities have suggested that the twin transition zone be used to designate the range in elemental concentration that exists between deficiency and sufficiency. Others have termed this range in concentration the critical nutrient range (CNR). This concentration range lies within the transition zone, a range in concentration in which a 0 to 10% reduction in yield occurs, with the 10% reduction in yield point specified as the critical value of the element.

In a plant analysis diagnosis based on either critical or standard values or sufficiency ranges, the plant part and time of sampling must be identical with that given for the source of the interpretative data since differences in plant part, stage of growth, genotype, and geographical location can result in significant variations in the elemental concentration found in the plant. Therefore, these traditional techniques of plant analysis interpretation have their limitations.

DRIS

An entirely different concept of plant analysis interpretation is the Diagnosis and Recommendation Integrated System (DRIS) (see book by Beverly in Appendix B). The DRIS technique of interpretation is based on a comparison of calculated elemental ratio indices with established norms. The DRIS approach was designed to:

- Provide a valid diagnosis irrespective of plant age or tissue origin
- Rank nutrients in their limiting order
- Stress the importance of nutrient balance

DRIS is based on the principle of elemental interrelationships by determining, in descending order, those elements from the most to the least limiting. The survey approach, utilizing the world's published literature in order to plot elemental leaf concentration versus yield, is used to develop a distribution curve. In order to normalize the distribution curve, the yield component is divided into low- and high-yield groups. Investigators have suggested that the data bank for determining DRIS norms consist of at least several thousand entries and be randomly selected. They also propose that at least 10% of the population be in the high-yield subgroup. The cut-off value selected divides the low- from the high-yielding subgroups so that the high-yield data subgroup remains normally distributed for selecting the elemental concentration mean, ratio, and product of the elemental means. The ratio or product selected for calculating DRIS norms is the one with the largest variance that maximizes the diagnostic sensitivity.

Although the DRIS method of interpretation has been based primarily on the major elements, other DRIS indices have been generated that include the micronutrients boron (B), copper (Cu), iron (Fe), manganese (Mn), and zinc (Zn). The system emphasizes the major elements, since the database for the major elements is considerably larger than the database for the micronutrients. Thus, a micronutrient DRIS indice would be less reliable than one for a major element.

The DRIS concept of plant analysis interpretation has been compared to the sufficiency range interpretative values used in the more traditional techniques. In general, most interpreters agree that both methods of interpretation have their advantages, but seem at times to work best when used together.

DRIS apparently works best at the extremes of the sufficiency range by pinpointing insufficient elements or balances of elements. It is less useful when plant nutrient levels are well within the sufficiency range. In most studies that have been designed to test the DRIS concept, users have found that DRIS is not entirely independent of either location or time of sampling, and that DRIS diagnosis can frequently be misleading and incorrect. Therefore, it is doubtful that the DRIS method of plant analysis interpretation will ever be exclusively used in lieu of the more traditional critical value or sufficiency range techniques.

Experience Needed

None of the interpretative procedures discussed above is infallible, and all of these interpretative techniques are best used by the most experienced individuals. The interpretation of a plant analysis is still an art in which the interpreter must use all the resources available to evaluate the nutrient element status of the plant, and then design a corrective treatment when an insufficiency is uncovered based on the data, plus some degree of intuition. In addition, being able to observe the situation in the field can be invaluable. With video and digital cameras and computers, the interpreter can be supplied real-time visuals that can aid considerably when an interpretation seems difficult to make based only on the assay results.

Data Logging/Tracking

A useful but little used technique for plant analysis utilization is data logging or tracking, a technique based on a time series of analysis results. An example of seasonal tracking is the monitoring of the nitrate (NO_3) and phosphorus (P) levels in cotton petioles as shown in Figure 4.5. The objective for data logging or tracking is to regulate cultural practices so as to maintain plant elemental levels within the sufficiency range. The time plot of plant analysis results also warns of developing insufficiencies when the plotted slope of the time line begins to move toward either boundary line of the sufficiency range. Thus corrective measures can be taken before an insufficiency occurs, which may then lead to a reduction in yield and/or quality.

Plant Analysis Report Forms

Various formats are used to report a plant analysis result to the farmer/grower. Most forms are relatively simple and provide the analytical data along with an interpretation or explanation of the meaning of the test results, and a recommendation for either continuing current cultural practice(s) or needed corrective action.

Today, most plant analysis laboratories provide a number of interpretative values. An example is the University of Wisconsin Plant Analysis program, which provides the farmer with a sufficiency range interpretation designation (deficient, low, sufficient, high, or excessive) and a DRIS indice interpretation (Figure 4.6). Another trend today is to provide as much information as possible to the grower. For example, the Oregon State University Plant Analysis Laboratory reports long-term and yearly averages, and sufficiency ranges (Figure 4.7). All of these laboratories are providing as much

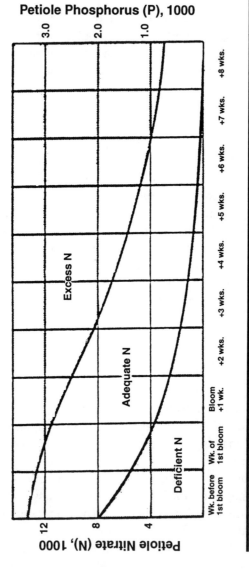

FIGURE 4.5 University of Georgia Cotton Petiole Monitoring Report form.

THIS REPORT FOR:

PLANT ANALYSIS REPORT
SAMPLES ANALYZED BY
SOIL AND PLANT ANALYSIS LABORATORY
5711 Mineral Point Road
Madison, WI 53705

COOPERATIVE EXTENSION PROGRAMS

P. A. HYBRID
P. A.
COBB, WIS. 53526

DATE 13-NOV-86

COUNTY IOWA

CROP CORN   FIELD DESIGNATION CORN F   LAB NOS. 9 - 10 ACCT. 999

IDENTIFICATION / PLANT ANALYSES FOR EACH SAMPLE

Sample No	Plant Appearance	N %	P %	K %	Ca %	Mg %	S %	Zn ppm	B ppm	Mn ppm	Fe ppm	Cu ppm	Al ppm	Na ppm
1	NORMAL	2.73	0.30	0.74	0.53	0.48	0.22	23	9	52	128	9.7	107	47
2	ABNORMAL	2.83	0.34	0.27	0.74	1.44	0.25	24	12	110	601	11.2	790	20

D = Deficient. L = Low. S = Sufficient. H = High. E = Excessive

INTERPRETATION OF PLANT ANALYSIS BY THE DIAGNOSIS AND RECOMMENDATIONS INTEGRATED SYSTEM (DRIS)

Sample No		DEFICIENT	LOW	SUFFICIENT	HIGH
1	Element DRIS Index	K -48		S ZN N P CA B CU MN -5 -5 -3 -2 1 2 3 3	MG 53
2	Element DRIS Index	K -271		ZN N S P -3 -2 4 10	B CU CA MN 11 12 18 42

SOIL ANALYSES FOR EACH SAMPLE / FERTILIZER APPLIED

Sample No	Soil pH	Est CEC	Organic Matter T/A	P Lbs/A	K Lbs/A	Ca Lbs/A	Mg Lbs/A	S Lbs/A	Zn Lbs/A	B Lbs/A	Mn Lbs/A
1	6.7			38	65 H	135 L					
2	6.2			36	52 H	120 L					

V = Very Low L = Low LM = Low-Medium M = Medium HM = High-Medium H = High E = Excessive

	Bdct.	Row	Side dress	Lbs/A
N	X	X		131
P₂O₅		X		24
K₂O		X		24

Secondary and Micronutrients

REMEDIAL FERTILIZER RECOMMENDATIONS FOR EACH SAMPLE

Sample No	N Lbs/A	P₂O₅ Lbs/A	K₂O Lbs/A	Mg Lbs/A	S Lbs/A	Zn Lbs/A	B Lbs/A	Mn Lbs/A	Fe Lbs/A	Cu Lbs/A
1	80									
2										

Herbicides NO
Insecticides NO
Fungicides NO

WEATHER
Below Normal — Normal — Above Normal

SUPPLEMENTAL SAMPLE INFORMATION

Date Sampled 07/09/85	Plant Part LEAF	Soil Series DODGEVILLE	Rainfall X
Date Planted 05/09/85	Plant Position LEAF	Drainage 600B Irrigated	Temperature X
Growth Stage WAIST HI	% Abnormal 80	Type of Drainage	Previous Crop CORN / Condition of Previous Crop POOR

COMMENTS:

These plants are low or deficient in nitrogen; possibly as a result of inadequate N or P fertilization; excessively wet soil conditions; excessive leaching on sandy soils or excessive K fertilization.

These plants are low or deficient in potassium. Possible causes of this are low K soil test levels; inadequate K fertilization; poor drainage or soil compaction.

These plants are excessive in iron and aluminum. This most likely results from contamination of the tissue with soil particles and does not reflect the true iron and aluminum content.

FARMER'S COPY

FIGURE 4.6 Wisconsin Cooperative Service Plant Analysis Report form.

PLANT ANALYSIS LABORATORY

DEPARTMENT OF HORTICULTURE

OREGON STATE UNIVERSITY

CORVALLIS, OREGON 97331

PLANT TISSUE ANALYSIS FOR:	ADDITIONAL COPY TO.	COUNTY AGENT:
Merlin C Monroe 8800 Cooper Spur Rd Parkdale OR 97041 COUNTY Hood River		David J Burkhart 2990 Exp. Station Dr Hood River OR 97031 386-3343

SAMPLE DATE	RECEIVED DATE	COMPLETION DATE	LAB NO.
8-20-90	9-5-90	10/19/1990	784

FIELD NAME OR GROWER SAMP. NO.	PLANT SAMPLED	VARIETY
#1	Pear	Anjou

PLANT ANALYSIS RESULTS   (PLEASE READ MATERIAL ON BACK)

		DEFICIENT	BELOW NORMAL	NORMAL	ABOVE NORMAL	EXCESS	AVERAGES THIS YEAR	LONG TERM
NITROGEN (N) % DW	2.07		XXXXXXXXXX				2.06	2.14
PHOSPHORUS (P) % DW	0.16		XXXXXXXXXX				0.17	0.16
POTASSIUM (K) % DW	1.37		XXXXXXXXXX				1.42	1.44
SULFUR (S) % DW	0.13		XXXXXXXXXX				0.13	0.14
CALCIUM (CA) % DW	2.48		XXXXXXXXXX				2.05	1.77
MAGNESIUM (MG) % DW	0.31		XXXXXXXXXX				0.32	0.29
MANGANESE (MN) PPM DW	48		XXXXXXXXXX				122	95
IRON (FE) PPM DW	118		XXXXXXXXXX				135	117
COPPER (CU) PPM DW	23		XXXXXXXXXX	XXX			12	10
BORON (B) PPM DW	26		XX				36	30
ZINC (ZN) PPM DW	47		XXXXXXXXXX				29	33

FIGURE 4.7   Oregon State University Plant Analysis Report form.

information as possible by means of the plant analysis report so that the farmer/grower can make an intelligent decision with regard to the use of agricultural chemicals required to maintain nutrient element sufficiency.

Utilization for Plant Nutrient Management

For many, a plant analysis result is viewed primarily as a diagnostic device for determining which element in a sampled and assayed plant is below or above the optimum concentration for normal plant growth. Five decades ago, four principal objectives for the utilization of a plant analysis result were put forth:

- To aid in determining the nutrient supplying power of the soil
- To aid in determining the effect of treatment on the nutrient supply in the plant
- To study relationships between the nutrient status of the plant and crop performance as an aid in predicting fertilizer requirements
- To help lay the foundation for approaching new problems or for surveying unknown regions to determine where critical plant nutritional experimentation should be conducted

None of these objectives satisfies the primary practical field use of a plant analysis today—to diagnose suspected elemental insufficiencies. However, the third objective mentioned seems to meet today's criteria for determining the fertilization needs of fruit and nut trees. In common use today are programs that base fertilizer recommendations on leaf analyses, particularly for perennials and plantation crops.

Using one or several of the systems of interpretation of a plant analysis result discussed above, the next step is to determine if an insufficiency exists and why, and then devise a treatment(s) to correct the insufficiency for the sampled crop, or to develop a strategy needed to prevent the insufficiency from occurring in a subsequent crop.

For example, if a magnesium (Mg) deficiency is confirmed by means of plant analysis, the interpreter must determine why it exists and what steps should be taken to correct the deficiency. The corrective action needed would be determined by factors such as the soil pH, level of soil available Mg, etc. Adding fertilizer Mg, for example, would be ineffective if the soil pH is less than 5.4. Soil fertility level, fertilizer applied, and general growing conditions, as is detailed on a plant history form (Figure 4.8), are vital to the assessment of a plant analysis result.

There are a number of publications that can provide users with interpretative plant analysis information (see Reference Text List, Appendix B). An example of how a plant analysis result can be interpreted for corn is given in Table 4.3.

Soil Testing

Recent soil test information can be particularly helpful to the interpreter of a plant analysis result. Therefore, soil samples should be taken at the time and in the same vicinity where plant tissue samples are collected, and the soil assay results should be included with the plant analysis data.

1785

PLANT ANALYSIS HISTORY FORM
The University of Georgia
Cooperative Extension Service
Soil Testing and Plant Analysis Laboratory
Athens, Georgia

GROWER

NAME (PRINT)	
ADDRESS	
CITY, STATE, ZIP CODE	
COUNTY AGENT	COUNTY

SULFUR TEST: (EXTRA FEE) ☐ YES ☐ NO

FOR LAB USE ONLY
Lab No. ______
Date Received ______
Date Returned ______
Invoice No. ______
or
Fee Received ______

CROP: ______
VARIETY OR HYBRID: ______
THIS IS SAMPLE NUMBER ______ OF ______ SAMPLES
DATE PLANTED: ______
DATE SAMPLED: ______
STAGE OF GROWTH: (CHECK ONE) SEEDLING ☐ EARLY GROWTH ☐ BLOOM ☐ FRUITING ☐ MATURE ☐
WHEAT (ENTER GROWTH STAGE NUMBER) ______
PLANT HEIGHT ______ INCHES

PLANT PART SAMPLED: (CHECK ONE)
☐ WHOLE PLANT ☐ STEMS ☐ PETIOLES
☐ LEAVES ☐ TOP 6" OTHER ______

POSITION ON PLANT: (CHECK ONE)
CORN ☐ EAR LEAF ☐ LEAF BELOW WHORL
OTHER CROPS ☐ UPPER ☐ MIDDLE ☐ LOWER

APPEARANCE OF PLANT:
☐ NORMAL ☐ ABNORMAL ______ DESCRIBE

PLANT POPULATION: ______
PLANT DISEASES? ☐ NO ☐ YES
PEST PROBLEM? ☐ NO ☐ YES
IRRIGATION: ______ INCHES APPLIED
☐ NONE ☐ CABLE TOW ☐ CENTER PIVOT
INJECTION SYSTEM: ☐ YES ☐ NO
RAINFALL: (LAST 3 WEEKS)
☐ BELOW NORMAL ☐ NORMAL ☐ ABOVE NORMAL
AIR TEMPERATURE: (LAST 3 WEEKS)
☐ BELOW NORMAL ☐ NORMAL ☐ ABOVE NORMAL

FERTILIZER APPLIED TO SAMPLED CROP:

METHOD		N lb/A	P_2O_5 lb/A	K_2O lb/A	Date Applied
Broadcast ☐ or	Before Planting				
Knifed In ☐	After Planting				
Row	Side Dress				
	Beside Seed				
Foliar					
Other					

micronutrients, insecticides, pesticides

Kind	Rate	Method	Date Applied

SOIL TEST DATA: DATE OF PREVIOUS TEST ______ 19____
WAS SOIL TEST BY GEORGIA LAB ☐ OR OTHER LAB ☐
pH ______ P lbs/A ______ K lbs/A ______
Ca lbs/A ______ Mg lbs/A ______ L.R. ______

SOIL EROSION: ☐ NONE ☐ MODERATE ☐ SLIGHT ☐ SEVERE
SOIL TEXTURE: ______ (CLAY, SILT LOAM, SAND)
DRAINAGE: ☐ POOR ☐ FAIR ☐ GOOD ☐ EXCESSIVE
WAS A SOIL SAMPLE ALSO TAKEN FROM THIS SAME AREA FOR:
1. SOIL TEST ☐ YES ☐ NO
2. NEMATODE ASSAY ☐ YES ☐ NO

FIGURE 4.8 Plant Analysis History Form (Plank, 1988; with permission).

TABLE 4.3   Interpretation and Recommendation of Corn Leaf Analysis: Dry Land Corn

Plant part and time: Leaf below the whorl prior to tasseling and ear leaf at tasseling collected before silks turn brown	

Element and sufficiency range	Interpretation and recommendation
Nitrogen (N) Leaf below whorl 3.00-3.50% Ear leaf 2.75 to 3.50%	Deficiency due to inadequate or ineffective N fertilization. When occurring prior to tasseling, sidedress with 50 to 75 lbs N/A. When occurring at silking, no corrective treatment is recommended.
Phosphorus (P) 0.25 to 0.45%	Deficiency due to low soil P and/or inadequate P fertilization. Corrective treatment not recommended. Soil test and follow soil test recommendation for next crop.
Potassium (K) Leaf below whorl 2.00 to 2.50% Ear leaf 1.75 to 2.25%	Deficiency due to low soil K and/or inadequate K fertilization. Corrective treatment not recommended. If K in the tissue is high, it is generally due to excessive K fertilization. Soil test and follow soil test recommendation. Avoid large applications of K fertilizer to prevent a possible inducement of a Mg deficiency. When plant is Mg deficient, the K level in usually high.
Calcium (Ca) 0.25 to 0.50%	Deficiency not likely to occur as soil Ca level must be extremely low for a deficiency to occur. Usually low soil Ca is associated with low soil pH. Deficiency can be corrected by liming to maintain soil pH at approximately 6.0. High Ca levels are due to a major element (N, P, or K) deficiency.
Magnesium (Mg) 0.13 to 0.30%	Deficiency occurs when soil Mg level and/or soil pH is low and when prolonged cool–wet growing conditions prevail early in the season. Deficiency can also be induced by heavy applications of N and K fertilizer. Corrective treatment may be ineffective unless applied well in advance of tasseling. If low Mg is detected, apply a foliar application of Mg using 0.30 to 0.40 lbs. Mg/A as magnesium sulfate in 20 to 25 gallons of water or if the soil pH is above 5.4 and the soil Mg level is low soil apply 25 lbs of Mg/A. If the soil pH is less than 5.4, corrective treatment is not recommended.
Sulfur (S) Leaf below whorl 0.17 to 0.50% Ear leaf 0.15 to 0.50%	Low S may occur on sandy coastal plain soils where high analysis S-free Leaf below whorl fertilizers have been applied for several years. Avoid low S levels by including a minimum of 10 lbs S/A in the fertilizer. Maintain the N:S ratio between 10:1 to 15:1 for optimum corn yields. When S is low in tissue, apply a minimum of 10 lbs S/A. If sidedress nitrogen has not been

TABLE 4.3   Interpretation and Recommendation of Corn Leaf Analysis: Dry Land Corn (continued)

Element and sufficiency range	Interpretation and recommendation
	applied, use a nitrogen–sulfur combination material that contains 3 to 5% S as the nitrogen source. If sidedress N has been applied, apply a foliar application of S using 10 to 20 lbs of ammonium sulfate or 1/2 to 1 gallon of ammonium thiosulfate in 30 to 50 gallons of water/A. The latter material may cause some foliar burn, but should not adversely affect yields.
Boron (B) 4 to 25 ppm	Deficiency not likely to occur, except on very sandy low, organic matter content soils. Boron deficiency generally results in poor ear formation. If low leaf B and poor ear development are noted, include B in future fertilizer programs at the rate of 1 lb B/A. Boron may be high in soils where B fertilizer has been applied for other crops. Boron levels in excess of 30 ppm are excessive. Since corn is quite sensitive to B, great care needs to be followed when this element is included in fertilizer treatments.
Copper (Cu) 3 to 15 ppm	Deficiency not likely to occur. High Cu levels may occur when soils have been treated with poultry or other animal manures.
Iron (Fe) 30 to 200 ppm	Deficiency not likely to occur. High Fe test results normally indicate soil or dust contamination. An accurate Fe determination can only be made with washed leaves. .
Manganese (Mn) 15 to 300 ppm	Deficiency not likely to occur except on sandy soils or soils high in organic matter with a pH of 6.5 or higher. The deficiency can be corrected by a foliar application of 1 to 2 lbs Mn/A as manganese sulfate or 0.5 to 1.0 lb Mn/A as manganese chelate in 20 to 25 gallons of water. High Mn is due to low soil pH and frequently associated with Mg deficiency (see Mg discussion).
Molybdenum (Mo) 0.1 to 3.0 ppm	Deficiency not likely to occur.
Zinc (Zn) 15 to 60 ppm	Deficiency may occur on sandy soils low in organic matter (<1%) and soils that are near neutral in pH. A deficiency can be corrected by foliar application of zinc at rates of 0.5 lb Zn/A as zinc sulfate or as zinc chelate in 20 to 25 gallons of water.
Aluminum (Al) less than 200 ppm	High Al levels occur when the soil is wet for long periods or the soil pH is extremely low. However, Al does not enter the plant easily after about 3 weeks after emergence. High Al may also be due to soil or dust contamination, in which case Fe is also usually high (see Fe discussion above).

From Plank, C.O. 1988. *Plant Analysis Handbook for Georgia.* Georgia Cooperative Extension Service, University of Georgia, Athens. With permission.

Comparative Samples

When collecting tissue from plants that show a suspected elemental insufficiency symptom, the collection of similar tissue from nearby plants without symptoms can be extremely helpful in the interpretation. In addition, the taking of soil samples in the vicinity of both types of plants is strongly recommended. By broadening the collection process (for both plants and soils), the interpreter is provided additional information that can be important when dealing with a suspected nutrient element insufficiency problem. Therefore, the interpretation and generated corrective recommendation are based not only on the assay of the symptom plants, but also on the input of the additional information provided by the other sets of analysis results.

Precision Farming

Probably no other aspect of plant nutrient management has attracted as much attention in the last several years as that associated with what has been coined precision farming, the design of detailed cropland maps based on a combination of grid soil sampling, aerial photography, and on-the-go yield determinations. Using a global positioning system (GPS), site-specific maps can be drawn in order to correlate soil characteristics (fertility, topography, drainage, etc.) to crop yield. Although detailed soil sampling, referred to as grid sampling, is required, grid plant sampling has not been included as a factor in precision farming systems. However, infrared photography can be used to observe plant canopy characteristics, characteristics that may be related to a particular stress condition. However, research is still needed to make infrared images meaningful in terms of the nutrient element status of the photographed crop. When changes in canopy characteristics are noted, assaying plants in specific areas can help to verify nutrient element needs and to assist in the development of lime and fertilizer treatments for correcting identified insufficiencies. Therefore, the role of plant analyses is to assist in the identification and development of correction measures at site-specific locations, adding another source of input for carrying out the objectives of a precision nutrient element management plan.

CHAPTER 5

Tissue Testing

Purpose

The two primary objectives in conducting a tissue test are:

1. To quickly identify the nutritional status of the plant for verification of an apparent nutrient element insufficiency
2. To determine, by evaluating the current nutrient-element status of the plant, whether additional fertilizer is needed to ensure the desired yield goal is obtained

Factors that distinguish a tissue test from a plant analysis are:

- A tissue test is conducted in the field rather than collecting tissue that will be sent to a laboratory for analysis.
- A tissue test is conducted on extracted sap; a plant analysis is the determination of the total elemental content, made by extraction on oven-dried, ground plant tissue.

In general, a tissue test is conducted using chemically treated papers or test strips, test tubes or vials, and specially prepared reagents. The development of a color and its intensity are used as indicators of the presence of an element (normally its ion) and its concentration, respectively. A change in color with the addition (by drop count or pipette volume) of a reagent is also used for concentration determination. Kits such as the HACH Kits are available that can be used to conduct such tests.

There have been new developments in instrumentation that can also be used to conduct a tissue test, such as hand-held, battery-operated specific-ion meters for the determination of the nitrate (NO_3^-) anion, and the cations potassium (K^+) and calcium (Ca^{2+}). A more recent development has been the use of a chlorophyll meter that measures the greenness of plant tissue, readings that can be correlated with the nutrient-element status of the plant, primarily for the assessment of the nitrogen (N) status of a plant.

Sampling Techniques

In order to successfully conduct most tissue tests, a sufficient quantity of cell sap must be obtained in order to conduct the test. Conductive tissues, such as leaf petioles, leaf mid-ribs, or the plant stalk itself are commonly selected. The petiole or mid-rib tissues are collected from the recently matured leaves. When the plant stalk is the test tissue, the stalk section at the base of the plant or the mid-section is the portion of the stalk selected.

The time of sampling is determined by the purpose for the tissue test. For diagnostic evaluation—when dealing with a suspected nutrient-element insufficiency—the best time is when the first symptoms of stress are visually evident. For determining nutrient-element status—when the need for supplemental fertilization is to be determined—the time of sampling is based on a specific development period in the life cycle of the plant.

Here are some general instructions to be followed when collecting plant tissue for testing:

- Collect tissue between 8:00 A.M. and 5:00 P.M.
- Do not collect tissue immediately after a rain
- Collect tissue from young plants to those near maturity
- Do not collect tissue from plants during drought or when the plants are under some stress condition

Testing Procedures

The type of tests to be conducted and the kit selected will determine to a considerable degree which procedure will be used to assay the collected tissue; therefore, only general instructions can be specified.

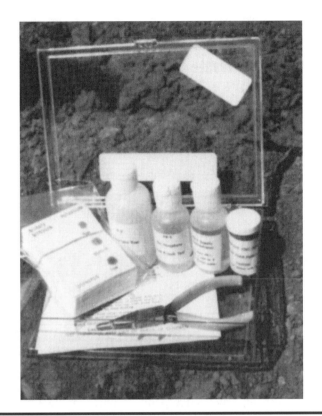

FIGURE 5.1 The PLANT CHECK Tissue Testing Kit.

A commonly used tissue testing kit, PLANT CHECK (Figure 5.1), consists of a pack of test papers and the reagents required for the determination of nitrate-nitrogen (NO_3-N), phosphorus (P) as the phosphate anion (PO_4^{3-}), and potassium (K). All three determinations can be made on one test paper (Figure 5.2). The test procedures for the PLANT CHECK kit are given in Table 5.1.

General Test Procedures for Paper and Vial-Type Kits

From a collected petiole or leaf mid-rib, and using pliers, an aliquot of sap is squeezed onto the test paper in the area marked "Phosphorus," and then

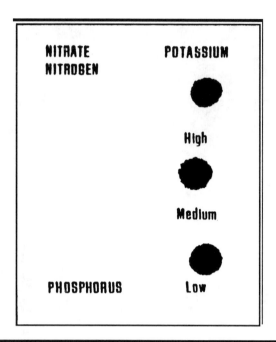

FIGURE 5.2 Tissue Testing Paper from the PLANT CHECK Testing Kit.

additional aliquots of squeezed sap on to each of the three spots below "Potassium."

Nitrate-Nitrogen Test

A short section of mid-rib or petiole is placed across the end of the test paper marked "Nitrate Nitrogen," a small aliquot of nitrate powder sprinkled along the piece of tissue, the paper folded over, and the area squeezed with the pliers, squeezing until sufficient to wet the area on the test paper with sap. If nitrate (NO_3) is present, the powder will turn red, the speed of color development and its intensity (pink = low; red = high) indicates the concentration of NO_3 present.

Phosphorus Test

On the sap-wetted spot on the test paper designated "Phosphorus," two drops of Phosphorus Reagent 1 are placed followed by two drops of Phospho-

TABLE 5.1   Tissue Testing Directions for Use of the PLANT CHECK Tissue Testing Kit (use these testing materials in year of purchase only)

SETTING UP THE KIT
Your kit contains the following:

Potassium test papers	Pk-1 bottle
Nitrate powder	P-2 bottle
Extracting pliers	Pk-1 concentrate supply

You need to obtain distilled water from a drug store, bottling company, or a laboratory. Add distilled water to the shoulder of each the PK-1 and P-2 bottles. Your kit is now ready to use.

PLANT SAMPLING

When: From 8:00 a.m. to 5:00 p.m.
Not immediately after a rain.
From young plant. to near maturity.
Not during drought or other stress conditions.

Part of Plant (see Chart):   Mid-rib or petiole of recently matured leaf (avoid old at bottom, young at top). Stalk, midway up plant.

Part of Field: Avoid bad spots except for comparison. Test enough plants to determine definite pattern of levels.

TESTING PROCEDURE
Nitrate Test

On Plant: Split stalk, mid-rib, or petiole. Add small amount (match-head size) of nitrate powder to cut tissue and work into sap with knife blade. Wait 5 minutes for final reading.

On Test Paper: Fold the corner of paper and place a section of plant tissue and the same amount of nitrate powder as given above in fold. Squeeze fold until sap contacts powder. Wait 5 minutes for final reading.

In Vials: Mash the equivalent of 1/8 teaspoon of tissue with pliers, place in vial in 5 mL of water. Stir one minute, add pea-size portion of the nitrate powder. Shake and allow 5 minutes for reaction.

READING
No color or white—Very Low
Pink—Low
Light red—Medium
Cherry red—High

Phosphorus Test

On Test Paper: Squeeze small amount of sap from cut end of tissue onto filter paper. Add small drop of PK-1, then a large drop of P-2.

In Vials: Place 5 mL of PK-1 solution in the vial. Mash and stir tissue as for the Nitrate Test. Stir for 1 minute, add a drop of P-2 or stir with a tin rod.

TABLE 5.1   Tissue Testing Directions for Use of the PLANT CHECK Tissue Testing Kit (use these testing materials in year of purchase only) (continued)

READING
No color—Very Low
Light Blue— Low
Medium Blue—Medium
Intense Blue—High

Potassium Test
On Test Paper: Squeeze small amount of sap on each of the orange test dots. Allow 30 to 40 seconds for reaction to take place. Then wash each dot with PK-1 (not an excess) to remove all orange color that will go.

READING
Orange left on sap spot, all 3 dots—High
Orange left on medium and low sap spots— Medium
Orange left on low sap spot—Low
No orange color left—Very Low

CONSTANTLY CHECK YOUR CHEMICALS

Summer heat, light, and contamination can cause your chemicals to deteriorate. Check them as follows:

Nitrate Powder Should be white in color, not grey or pink.

Phosphorus Solution: Saliva is high in phosphate (PO_4). Check solutions by moistening filter paper with tongue. Run phosphorus test on this and on a blank spot (no phosphorus). Either no reaction where phosphate is present or color reaction where it is not, calls for a change of solutions. Simply wash bottles, add PK-1 concentrate from supply bottle to bottom mark and distilled water to shoulder. For new P-2 solution, place contents of one capsule in P-2 bottle and add distilled water to fill the bottle.

Potassium Paper: Dots should be bright orange in color. When washed with PK-1, the dots should be yellow, not brownish.

rus Reagent 2. The appearance of a blue color, its speed of development and intensity (pale blue-low; dark blue-high) indicates the presence of P and its probable concentration, respectively.

Potassium Test

Using Phosphorus Reagent No. 2, place two drops on each of the three Potassium Orange dots on the test paper. If an orange precipitate remains, this indicates the presence of K. Of the three tests possible with this kit, the K test is the only defined quantitative test.

Nitrate-Nitrogen Stalk Test

For a crop plant such as corn, cut a 3- to 4-inch section of stalk from the base of the plant, cut the stalk section in half, and then place some nitrate powder on the open cut. Put the two halves together, moving them so as to mix the powder with the exposed stalk cut. After about one minute, open the two halves. If nitrate (NO_3) is present, the intensity of the red color (pink = low; red = high) is a measure of its probable concentration.

Phosphorus Stalk Test

For a crop plant such as corn, cut a 3- to 4-inch section of stalk at the base. Cut the stalk section in half, and place two to three drops of Phosphorus Reagent No. 1 on the open cut, followed by two to three drops of Phosphorus Reagent No. 2. Put the two halves together, moving them so as to mix the added reagents with the exposed stalk cut. In about a minute, open the two halves. If P is present at a minimum concentration, a blue color will indicate its presence and the intensity of the blue color (pale blue = low; dark blue = high) will indicate its probable concentration.

Similar tests can be conducted using vials, other types of test papers, and electronic meters. Some of these test procedures have an advantage because they are quantitative, a requirement that is essential when a supplemental fertilizer application may be made based on the concentration found at a specified period in the growth of the plant. Two examples are the determination of the nitrate-nitrogen (NO_3-N) content at the base of the wheat plant stem, and the petiole NO_3-N content in a specifically selected cotton plant petiole. The NO_3-N content found would then determine how much additional N fertilizer needs to be applied.

Reagents

Refills for most of the reagents used in tissue testing kits can be obtained from the supplier of the kit. The recipes for making some of these reagents are given in Table 5.2.

Chlorophyll Meters

Another method of evaluating the nutrient-element status of a plant (primarily its N status) is with the use of a chlorophyll meter; the most commonly used is the Minolta SPAD 502 Chlorophyll Meter (Figure 5.3). The meter offers the user an easy non-destructive measurement of the greenness of a selected leaf. The reliability of the meter reading is based on the degree of association between the plant's nutrient-element status and the meter reading that is obtained based on the green color of the leaf selected. There have been a number of reports published in the last several years that describe the use of the meter versus the N plant status for several crops, mainly for corn as well as for wheat and rice.

Specific-Ion Nitrate Meter

A relatively quick method for determining the nitrate-nitrogen (NO_3-N) level in petiole cell sap is with the use of a specific ion meter, such as the Cardy meter shown in Figure 5.4. The procedure is as follows:

- Collect a representative sample of leaf or petiole tissue.
- Using a sap press (garlic press), squeeze an aliquot of sap onto a clean smooth plastic surface.
- Transfer an aliquot of the sap directly onto the meter sensor and read the NO_3-N concentration.

Using a reference source relating nitrate-nitrogen (NO_3-N) content with N plant status, compare the meter reading obtained with the reference to determine if the concentration found is within the sufficiency range for the plant part being tested, type of crop, and stage of crop development.

TABLE 5.2   Preparation of Reagents for Conducting Tissue Tests Using a Filter Paper

Nitrate-Nitrogen (NO_3-N)

Reagent	100 grams dry barium sulfate ($BaSO_4$), 10 grams manganese sulfate ($MnSO_4 \cdot H_2O$), 2 grams of finely powdered zinc (Zn), 75 grams citric acid, 4 grams sulfanic acid, and 2 grams of ∂-naphthylamine are finely ground as separate portions with a mortar and pestle, then thoroughly mix and stored in a blackened container.
Reaction	Any degree of red color produced on reaction with plant sap indicates the presence of nitrate (NO_3).

Phosphorus (P)

Solution A	10 grams ammonium molybdate [$(NH_4)_6Mo_7O_{24} \cdot 4H_2O$] are dissolved in 85 mL water.
Solution B	Mix 16 mL water with 170 mL concentrated hydrochloric acid (HCl).
Concentrated solution	Mix Solution A and B and add 2 grams boric acid (H_3BO_3) per 50 mL of the mixed solution.
Working solution	Dilute the concentrated solution 10 times with water.
Reduction suspension	Place tin chloride ($SnCl_2 \cdot 2H_2O$) in a small dropping bottle and add water.

Potassium (K)

Solution A	Add 0.6 grams dipicrylamine (2,2',4,4',6,6'-hexanitrodiphenylamine) and 0.6 grams of sodium carbonate (Na_2CO_3) to 25 mL water and boil for 10 minutes.
Solution B	Dilute 8 mL of Solution A to 25 mL with water.
Solution C	Dilute 10 mL of Solution B to 15 mL with water.
Preparation of filter paper	Three separate 8-mm diameter spots, one from each Solution, A, B, and C, are placed on a filter paper and allowed to dry.

FIGURE 5.3 The Minolta SPAD 502 Chlorophyll Meter (courtesy of Spectrum Technologies, Inc.).

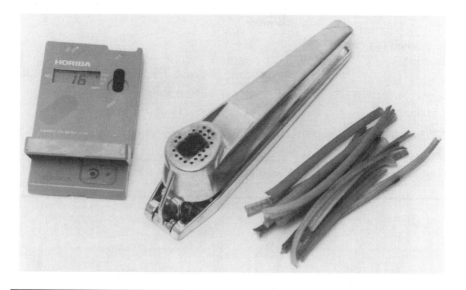

FIGURE 5.4 The Cardy Nitrate Meter, Garlic Press, and Plant Petioles (courtesy of Spectrum Technologies, Inc.).

Although the nitrate meter is only one of several perfected specific-ion meters available today, rapid developments are being made to develop meters that can be used for the determination of ions, such as potassium (K), sodium (Na), and calcium (Ca).

Methods of Interpretation

Interpretation of a tissue test result can be difficult for the inexperienced. Therefore, it is important to gain some practical experience in the field— testing plants in various stages of development and nutrient-element stress— before venturing forth under critical situations when a test result will form the basis for corrective action.

With most tissue testing kits and instruments, instructions are provided with the kit as well as some interpretation information based on obtained test results. Before this given interpretative information is to be used, some verification may be required based on trial tests by the user as was stated above.

An example of test interpretation information provided with the PLANT CHECK Tissue Testing Kit is given in Table 5.3.

When and How to Use Tissue Tests (from the PLANT CHECK Kit)

The procedures given below are applicable to any tissue testing procedure, no matter what test kit or device will be used to conduct the test.

1. Use tissue test results along with all other available information— soil tests, past history, visual observations, current fertilizer use, etc.— to determine adequacy or inadequacy of nutrient supplies.
2. Look for the one factor that is most limiting plant growth. Be careful—it may not be nitrogen (N), phosphorus (P), or potassium (K).
3. Use tissue tests to increase your knowledge of plant nutrition.
4. Remember that the plant is a dynamic biological system, and that nutrients [particularly nitrate-nitrogen (NO_3-N) and K] can be present in adequate amounts today only to be short a month from now because the soil could not supply them fast enough. Test often.

TABLE 5.3 Sampling and Interpretation Chart for Use with the PLANT CHECK Tissue Testing Kit

Plant	Test	Part to sample	Minimum level to avoid hidden hunger
Corn			
Under 15"	NO_3	Mid-rib, basal leaf	High
	PO_4	Mid-rib, basal leaf	Medium
	K	Mid-rib, basal leaf	High
15" to ear showing	NO_3	Base of stalk	High
	PO_4	Mid-rib, 1st mature leaf	Medium
	K	Mid-rib, 1st mature leaf	High
Ear to very early dent	NO_3	Base of stalk	
	PO_4	Mid-rib, leaf below ear	Medium
	K	Mid-rib, leaf below ear	Medium
Soybean			
Early growth to mid-season	NO_3	Not tested	
	PO_4	Pulvinus (swollen base of petiole), 1st mature leaf	High
	K		High
Mid-season to good pod development	PO_4	Pulvinus, 1st mature leaf	Medium
	K	Pulvinus, 1st mature leaf	Medium
Cotton			
Early bloom	NO_3	Petiole, basal leaf	High
	PO_4	Petiole, basal leaf	High
	K	Petiole, basal leaf	High
Bloom to boll set	NO_3	Petiole, 1st mature leaf	High
	PO_4	Petiole, 1st mature leaf	Medium
	K	Petiole, 1st mature leaf	High
Boll set to early early maturity	NO_3	Petiole, 1st mature leaf	Medium
	PO_4	Petiole, 1st mature leaf	Medium
Alfalfa			
Before 1st cutting	PO_4	Middle section of stem	High
	K	Middle section of stem	High
Before other cuttings	PO_4	Middle section of stem	High
	K	Middle section of stem	High
Small grains			
Shoot stage to milk stage	NO_3	Lower stem	High
	PO_4	Lower stem	Medium
	K	Lower stem	Medium

Sources for Tissue Testing Kits and Supplies

Testing Kits

HACH Company
P.O. Box 389
Loveland, Colorado 80539

Spectrum Technologies, Inc.
23839 West Andrew Road
Plainfield, Illinois 60544

LaMotte Chemical Products Company
P.O. Box 329
Chestertown, Maryland 21620

Test Papers

EM SCIENCE
480 Democrat Road
Gibbstown, New Jersey 08027

Electronic Meters

Spectrum Technologies, Inc.
23839 West Andrew Road
Plainfield, Illinois 60544

APPENDIX **A**

List of References by Chapter

Chapter 1: Plant Nutrition Basics

Arnon, A.I. and P.R. Stout. 1939. The essentiality of certain elements in minute quantity for plants with special reference to copper. *Plant Physiology* 14:371–375.

Barber, S.A. 1995. *Soil Nutrient Bioavailability: A Mechanistic Approach.* Second Edition. John Wiley & Sons, Chichester, NY.

Bélanger, R.R., P.A. Brown, D.L. Ehret, and J.G. Menzies. 1995. Soluble silicon: Its role in crop and disease management of greenhouse crops. *Plant Disease* 79:329–335.

Brown, P.H., R.M. Welsh, and E.E. Cary. 1987. Nickel: A micronutrient essential for higher plants. *Plant Physiology* 85:801–803.

Carson, E.W. (ed.). 1974. *The Plant Root and Its Environment.* University Press of Virginia, Charlottesville, VA.

Glass, A.D.M. 1989. *Plant Nutrition: An Introduction to Current Concepts.* Jones and Barlett Publishers, Boston, MA.

Epstein, E. 1965. Mineral nutrition, pp. 438–466. In: J. Bonner and J.E. Varner (eds.), *Plant Biochemistry.* Academic Press, Inc., Orlando, FL.

Epstein, E. 1994. The anomaly of silica in plant biology. *Proc. Natl. Acad. Sci. (USA)* 91:11–17.

Kabata-Pendias, A. and H. Pendias. 1994. *Trace Elements in Soils and Plants.* Second Edition. CRC Press, Inc., Boca Raton, FL.

Markert, B. 1994. Plants as biomonitors—Potential advantages and problems, pp. 601– 613. In: D.C. Adriano, Z.S. Chen, and S.S. Yang (eds.), *Biogeochemistry of Trace Elements.* Science and Technology Letters. Northwood, New York.

Melsted, S.W. 1973. Soil-plant relationships (some practical considerations in waste management). In: *Proceedings Joint Conference on Recycling Municipal Sludges and Effluents on Land.* University of Illinois, Urbana.

Mengel, K. and E.A. Kirkby. 1987. *Principles of Plant Nutrition.* Fourth Edition. International Potash Institute, Berne, Switzerland.

Marschner, H. 1986. *Mineral Nutrition in Higher Plants.* Academic Press, Inc., New York.

Pais, I. 1983. The biological importance of titanium. *J. Plant Nutr.* 6:3–131.

Pais, I. and J.B. Jones, Jr. 1996. *Handbook on Trace Elements in the Environment.* St. Lucie Press, Boca Raton, FL.

Takahnashi, E., J.F. Ma, and Y. Miyake. 1990. The possibility of silicon as an essential element for higher plants, pp. 99–122. In: *Comments on Agriculture and Food Chemistry.* Gordon and Breach Science Publishers, London, Great Britain.

Chapter 2: The Major Elements

IFA World Fertilizer Use Manual. 1992. International Fertilizer Industry Association, Paris, France.

Ludwick, A.E. (ed.). 1990. *Western Fertilizer Handbook—Horticultural Edition.* Interstate Publishers, Inc., Danville, IL.

Maynard, D.N., A.V. Barker, P.L. Minotti, and N.H. Peck. 1976. Nitrate accumulation in vegetables. *Adv. Agron.* 28:71–118.

Chapter 3: The Micronutrients

Bergmann, W. 1983. *Ernähruggstörungen bei Kulturpflanzen, Entstehung und Diagnose.* Gustav Fischer Verlag, Jena , Germany.

Bergmann, W. and P. Neubert. 1976. *Pflanzendiagnose und Pflanzenanalyse.* Fischer, Jena, Germany.

Kabata-Pendias, A. and H. Pendias. 1994. *Trace Elements in Soils and Plants.* Second Edition. CRC Press, Boca Raton, FL.

Melsted, S.W. 1973. Soil-plant relationships (some practical considerations in waste management). In: *Proceedings Joint Conference on Recycling Municipal Sludges and Effluents on Land.* University of Illinois, Urbana.

Porter, J.R. and D.W. Lawlor, (eds.). 1991. *Plant Growth Interactions with Nutrition and Environment.* Society for Experimental Biology. Seminar Series 43. Cambridge Press, New York, NY.

Romheld, V. and H. Marshner. 1991. Function of micronutrients in plants, pp. 297–328. In: J.J. Mortvedt et al. (eds.). *Micronutrients in Agriculture,* 2nd Edition. SSSA Book Series No. 4. Soil Science Society of America, Madison, WI.

Chapter 4: Plant Analysis

Armstrong, D.L. 1996. Transition to precision. *Better Crops with Plant Food* 80(3). 1–40

Beverly, R.B. 1991. *A Practical Guide to the Diagnosis and Recommendation Integrated System (DRIS).* Micro-Macro Publishing, Athens, GA.

Jones, J.B., Jr. 1970. Distribution of fifteen elements in corn leaves. *Commun. Soil Sci. Plant Anal.* 1:27–33.

Kalra, Y. (ed.). in press. *Plant Analysis Handbook.* St. Lucie Press, Boca Raton, FL.

Krantz, B.A., W.L. Nelson, and L.F. Burkhart. 1948. Plant-tissue tests as a tool in agronomic research, pp. 137–156. In: H.B. Kitchen (ed.), *Diagnostic Techniques for Soils and Crops.* The American Potash Institute, Washington, D.C.

Mills, H.A. and J.B. Jones, Jr. 1997. *Plant Analysis Handbook* II. Micro-Macro Publishing, Athens, GA.

Okhi, K. 1987. Critical nutrient levels related to initial deficiency and toxicity levels for sorghum. *J. Plant Nutr.* 10:1583–1590.

Plank, C.O. 1988. *Plant Analysis Handbook for Georgia.* Georgia Cooperative Extension Service, University of Georgia, Athens.

Reuter, D.J. and J.B. Robinson (eds.). 1997. *Plant Analysis: An Interpretation Manual,* 2nd edition. CSIRO Publishing, Collingwood, Australia.

Smith, P.F. 1962. Mineral analysis in plant tissue. *Annu. Rev. Plant Physiol.* 13:81–108.

Walinga, I. et al. 1995. *Plant Analysis Manual,* Kluwar Academic Publishers, Dordrecht, The Netherlands.

Chapter 5: Tissue Testing

Syltie, P.W., S.W. Melsted, and W.M. Walker. 1972. Rapid tissue tests as indicators of yield, plant composition, and fertility for corn and soybeans. *Commun. Soil Sci. Plant Anal.* 3:37–49.

APPENDIX B

List of Reference Texts

Soils and Plants

Adriano, D.C. 1986. *Trace Elements in the Terrestrial Environment.* Springer-Verlag, New York.

Barber, S.A. 1995. *Soil Nutrient Bioavailability: A Mechanistic Approach.* Second Edition. John Wiley & Sons, Chichester, NY.

Chapman, H.C. 1966. *Diagnostic Criteria of Plants and Soils.* Division of Agriculture, University of California, Riverside.

Davidescu, D. and V. Davidescu. 1972. *Evaluation of Fertility by Plant and Soil Analysis.* Abacus Press, Kent, England.

Kabata-Pendias, A. and H. Pendias. 1995. *Trace Elements in Soils and Plants.* Revised Edition. CRC Press, Boca Raton, FL.

Lorenz, O.A. and D.N. Maynard. 1988. *Knotts Handbook for Vegetable Growers.* Third Edition. John Wiley & Sons, New York.

Ludwick, A.E. (ed.). 1990. *Western Fertilizer Handbook—Horticulture Edition.* Interstate Publishers, Inc., Danville, IL.

Mortvedt, J.J. (ed.). 1991. *Micronutrients in Agriculture. 1991.* Second Edition. SSSA Book Series No. 4. Soil Science Society of America, Madison, WI.

119

Mortvedt, J.J., P.M. Giordano and W.L. Lindsay. (eds.). 1972. *Micronutrients in Agriculture.* Soil Science Society of America, Madison, WI.

Nickolas, D.J.D. and A.R. Egan (eds.). 1975. *Trace Elements in Soil-Plant-Animal Systems.* Academic Press, Inc., New York.

Pais, I. and J. B. Jones, Jr. 1996. *Trace Elements in the Environment.* St. Lucie Press, Boca Raton, FL.

Sillanpää, M. 1972. *Trace Elements in Soils and Agriculture.* Soils Bulletin No. 17. FAO of the United Nations, Rome, Italy.

Sillanpää, M. 1990. *Micronutrient Assessment at the Country Level: An International Study.* Soil Bulletin 63. FAO of the United Nations, Rome, Italy.

Sillanpää, M. and H. Jansson. 1992. *Status of Cadmium, Lead, Cobalt, and Selenium in Soils and Plants of Thirty Countries.* Soil Bulletin 65. FAO of the United Nations, Rome, Italy.

Walsh, L.M. and J.D. Beaton (eds.). 1972. *Soil Testing and Plant Analysis.* Revised Edition. Soil Science Society of America, Madison, WI.

Westerman, R.L. (ed.). 1990. *Soil Testing and Plant Analysis.* Third Edition. SSSA Book Series No. 3. Soil Science Society of America, Madison, WI.

Plants

Barber, S.A. and D.R. Bouldin (eds.). 1984. *Roots, Nutrient and Water Influx, and Plant Growth.* ASA Special Publication No. 49. American Society of Agronomy, Madison, WI.

Bennett, W.F. 1993. *Nutrient Deficiencies and Toxicities in Crop Plants.* APS, The American Phytopathological Society, St. Paul, MN.

Bergmann, W. 1992. *Nutritional Disorders of Plants: Development, Visual and Analytical Diagnosis.* Gustav Pischer Verlag, Jena, Germany.

Bould, C., E.J. Hewitt and P. Needham. 1984. *Diagnosis of Mineral Disorders in Plants: Principles.* Volume 1. Chemical Publishing Co., New York.

Childers, N.F. (ed.). 1968. *Fruit Nutrition: Temperate to Tropical.* Horticultural Publications, Rutgers—The State University, New Brunswick, NJ.

Glass, A.D.M. 1898. *Plant Nutrition: An Introduction to Current Concepts.* Jones and Bartlett Publishers, Boston, MA.

Goodall, D.W. and P.G. Gregory. 1947. *Chemical Composition of Plants as an Index of their Nutritional Status.* Imperial Bureau Horticultural Plantation Crops. Technical Communications No. 17. Ministry of Agriculture, London, England.

Gough, L.P., H.T. Shacklette, and A.A. Case. 1979. *Element Concentrations Toxic to Plants, Animals, and Man.* Geological Survey Bulletin 1466. Department of the Interior. United States Government Printing Office, Washington, D.C.

Grundon, N.J. 1987. *Hungry Crops: A Guide to Nutrient Deficiencies in Field Crops.* Information Series Q187002. Queensland Department of Primary Industries, Brisbane, Australia.

Hardy, G.W. (ed.). 1967. *Soil Testing and Plant Analysis.* Plant Analysis, Part II. Special Publication No. 2. Soil Science Society of America, Madison, WI.

Jones, J.B., Jr. 1997. *Hydroponics: A Practical Guide for the Soilless Grower.* St. Lucie Press, Boca Raton, FL.

Lepp, N.W. (ed.). 1981. *Effect of Heavy Metal Pollution on Plants.* Applied Science Publications, London, England.

Martin-Prevel, P., J. Gagnard, and P. Gautier (eds.). 1987. *Plant Analysis: As a Guide to the Nutrient Requirements of Temperate and Tropical Crops.* Lavoisier Publishing Co., New York.

Marschner, H. 1986. *Mineral Nutrients in Higher Plants.* Academic Press, Inc., New York.

Mengel, K. and E.A. Kirkby. 1987. *Principles of Plant Nutrition.* Fourth Edition. International Potash Institute, Berne, Switzerland.

Mills, H.A. and J.B. Jones, Jr. 1996. *Plant Analysis Handbook II.* Micro-Macro Publishing, Inc., Athens, GA.

Plucknett, D.L. and H.B. Sprague. 1989. *Detecting Mineral Nutrient Deficiencies in Tropical and Temperate Crops.* Series No. 7. Westview Press, Boulder, CO.

Reuter, D.J. and J.B. Robinson (eds.). 1986. *Plant Analysis: An Interpretation Manual.* Inkata Press Pty Ltd., Victoria, Australia.

Roter, D.L. and J.B. Robinson (eds.) 1997. *Plant Analysis: An Interpretation Manual,* 2nd Edition. CSIRO Publishing, Collingwood, Australia.

Robb, D.A. and W.S. Pierpoint (eds.). 1983. *Metals and Micronutrients: Uptake and Utilization by Plants.* Phytochemical Society of Europe Symposia Series No. 21. Academic Press, Inc. New York.

Scaife, A. and M. Turner. 1984. *Diagnosis of Mineral Disorders in Plants: Vegetables.* Volume 2. Chemical Publishing Co., New York.

Shaw, A.J. (ed.). 1990. *Heavy Metal Tolerance in Plants: Evolutionary Aspects.* CRC Press, Boca Raton, FL.

Wallace, A. 1971. *Regulation of the Micronutrient Status of Plants by Chelating Agents and Other Factors.* UCLA 34P51-33, Arthur Wallace, Los Angeles, CA.

Winsor, G. and P. Adams. 1987. *Diagnosis of Mineral Disorders in Plants: Glasshouse Crops.* Volume 3. Chemical Publishing Co., New York.

APPENDIX C

Glossary

These definitions are defined in terms of their application to soil chemistry and plant nutrition, terms which may also have wider application, and therefore may be differently defined in other scientific disciplines.

Absorption—A process in which a substance is taken into something, such as a plant cell or structure by either and active (biological) or passive (physical or chemical) process.

Adsorption—The attachment of a substance to the surface of another substance.

Amino Acid—An organic acid containing an amino group (NH_2), and carboxyl group (COOH), and attached alkyl or aryl group.

Ammonium—A cation consisting of one nitrogen and four hydrogen atoms to form a cation whose formula is NH_4^+. The ammonium cation exists in the soil solution and on the soil's cation exchange complex and is combined with various anions to form nitrogen fertilizer sources [see Table 2.4].

Anion—An ion in solution having a negative charge. In chemical notation, the minus sign indicates the number of electrons the compound will give up.

Atom—The smallest unit of a substance that cannot be broken down further or changed to another substance by purely chemical means.

Atomic Weight—The average mass of a single atom of an element, expressed in terms of a dimensionless unit approximately equal to the mass of one hydrogen atom.

Atmospheric Demand—The capacity of air surrounding the plant to absorb moisture. This capacity of the air will influence the amount of water transpired by the plant through its exposed surfaces. Atmospheric demand varies with changing atmospheric conditions. It is greatest when air temperature and movement are high, and relative humidity is low. The reverse conditions exist when the atmospheric demand is low.

Availability—A term used to indicate that an element is in a form and position suitable for plant root absorption.

Base—Any compound that dissociates upon contact with water, releasing hydroxide ions.

Beneficial Elements—Elements not essential for plants but when present for plant use at specific concentrations enhance plant growth.

Boron (B)—An essential element classified as a micronutrient involved in energy transfer and carbohydrate movement. The element exists in the plant and soil solution as the borate anion (see Chapter 3).

Buffer Capacity—A measure of the ability to maintain a constant pH by neutralizing excess acids or bases.

Calcium (Ca)—An essential element classified as a major element which serves as a specific component of organic compounds and exists in the soil solution as a cation (see Chapter 2).

Catalyst—A substance whose presence causes or speeds up a chemical reaction between two or more other substance.

Cation—An ion have a positive charge. In chemical notation, the plus sign indicates the number of electrons the element will accept.

Chelates—A type of chemical compound in which a metallic atom (such as iron) is firmly combined with a molecule by means of multiple chemical bonds. The term refers to the claw of a crab, illustrative of the way in which the atom is held.

Chlorine (Cl)—An essential element classified as a micronutrient involved in the evolution of oxygen in photosystem II and raises cell osmotic pressure. Chlorine exists in the plant and soil solution as the chloride anion (see Chapter 3).

Chlorophyll—A complex molecule found in green plants that is the directly involved in photosynthesis (see Figure 1.2).

Chlorosis—A light green to yellow coloration of leaves or whole plants which usually indicates an essential element insufficiency or toxicity.

Colloid—A material that has been subdivided into extremely small particles capable of forming a colloidal suspension, particle size smaller than 0.001 millimeters (0.00004 inches) in diameter.

Copper (Cu)—An essential element classified as a micronutrient which participates in electron transport, and protein and carbohydrate metabolism. Copper exists in the plant and soil solution as the cupric cation (see Chapter 3).

Critical Value—A concentration value of an essential element below which deficiency occurs and above which sufficiency exists.

Deficiency—Describes the condition when an essential element is not in sufficient supply or proper form to adequately supply the plant, or not in sufficient concentration in the plant to meet the plant's physiological requirement. Plants usually grow poorly and show visual signs of abnormally in color and structure.

Denitrification—The conversion of organic or inorganic fixed nitrogen to nitrogen gas.

Diffusion—The movement of an ion in solution at high concentration to an area of lower concentration. Movement continues as long as the concentration gradient exists.

DRIS—An acronym for the Diagnosis and Recommendation Integrated System developed by Beaufils in 1973, which is based on nutrient relationships comparing an observed value compared to a corresponding ratio (see Reference Texts, *Appendix B*, Beverly reference).

Electron—A tiny charged particle, smallest of the three principle constituents of the atom, with a mass of 9.1×10^{-28} grams and a negative charge of 1.6×10^{-19} coulomb.

Element—A substance made up entirely of the same kind of atom.

Enzyme—An organic compound that serves as a catalyst in metabolic reactions. Enzymes are complex proteins that are highly specific to particular reactions.

Essential Elements—Those elements that are necessary for higher plants to complete their life cycle. Also, refers to the requirements established for essentially by Arnon and Stout in 1939 (see Chapter 1).

Evaporation—The conversion of a substance from the liquid state to the gaseous state. Evaporation occurs when a molecule of liquid gains sufficient energy (in the form of heat) to escape from the liquid into the atmosphere above it.

Evapotranspiration—The sum of evaporation and transpiration which varies with temperature, wind speed, type of vegetation, and relative humidity.

Fertilizer—A substance added to the soil/plant system to aid plant growth or increase productivity by providing extra nutrients for plant use.

Fibrous Root System—A plant root system consisting of a thick mat containing many short, slender, interwoven roots, without the presence of a taproot.

Free Space—That portion, about 10%, of plant roots into which ions in the soil solution can passively enter the root without passing through a membrane.

Gram—A unit of mass in the metric system, equivalent to the mass of one cubic centimeter of water at maximum density (4°C). There are 453.6 grams in an English pound.

Heavy Metals—A group of metallic elements with relatively high atomic weights (>55) that generally have similar effects on biological functions. Elements, such as, cadmium, chromium, lead, and mercury, are frequently identified as heavy metals.

Humidity—The amount of water vapor in the air. Relative humidity is the ratio of the air's actual water content to the total amount of water vapor the same volume of air could theoretically hold under its current conditions of temperature and pressure.

Humus—Organic materials within the soil that have been partially decomposed, forming a relatively stable organic matrix that has colloidal properties and in term, has a marked affect on the physical and chemical properties of a soil.

Hybrid—An organism whose male and female parents are members of two separate and distinct genetic lines.

Hydrocarbon—Any compound that contains only hydrogen and carbon in its molecular structure.

Hydrogen Bond—An electrostatic bond between an atom of hydrogen in one molecule and an atom of another element in a neighboring molecule.

Hydroponics—A method of growing plants without soil in which the essential elements are supplied by means of a nutrient solution that periodically baths the plant roots.

Hydroxide—Any inorganic compound containing hydrogen and oxygen bound together in the form of a negatively charged ion.

Ion—An atom that has lost or gained one or more electrons and has thus acquires a small positive or negative charge.

Ion Carriers—A proposed theory that explains how ions are transported from the surface of a root into root cells, the transport being across a membrane and a concentration gradient, the transport occurring by means of a carrier or carriers.

Ion Exchange—Refers to the phenomenon of physical-chemical attraction between charged colloidal substances (such as clay and humus) with cations and anions.

Ion Pumps—A proposed theory that explains how ions are transported from the surface of a root into root cells, the transport being across a membrane and a concentration gradient.

Iron (Fe)—An essential element classified as a micronutrient which is involved in the electronic transport systems in plants. Iron can exist as either the ferrous or ferric [cation in the plant or soil solution (see Chapter 3)].

Leaf Analysis—A method of determining the total elemental content of a leaf and relating this concentration to the well-being of the plant in terms of its elemental composition (see Chapter 4).

Lignin—A complex organic compound found as a constituent of the walls of plant cells.

Macronutrients—see *Major Essential Elements*

Magnesium (Mg)—An essential element classified as a major element which is a constituent of the chlorophyll molecule (see Figure 1.2) and serves as an enzyme cofactor for phosphorylation processes. Magnesium exists in the plant and soil solution as a cation (see Chapter 2).

Major Essential Elements—The nine essential elements found in relatively large concentrations in plant tissues. These elements are: calcium, carbon, hydrogen, oxygen, magnesium, nitrogen, phosphorus, potassium, and sulfur (see Chapter 2).

Manganese (Mn)—An essential element classified as a micronutrient which is involved in the oxidation-reduction processes and enzyme activator. Manganese exists in the plant and soil solution as a cation in several oxidation states (Mn^{+2}, Mn^{+3}, Mn^{+4}). The most common oxidation state is Mn^{+2} (see Chapter 3).

Mass Flow—The movement of ions as a result of the flow of water.

Metabolism—The set of chemical reactions taking place within the living cell that allows energy to be used and transferred and tissues to be constructed and repaired.

Metal—Any element that has a positive valence, that is, one that gives up electrons when forming ionic compounds.

Micronutrients—Seven essential elements found in relatively small concentrations in plant tissue. These elements are boron, chlorine, copper, iron, manganese, molybdenum, and zinc (see Chapter 3).

Mineral—A term used to identify an essential element.

Mineral Nutrition—The study of the essential elements as they relate to the growth and the well-being of plants.

Molecular Weight—The weight of one molecule, ion, group, or other formula unit. The molecular weight is the sum of the atomic weights of the atoms that combine to make up the formula unit.

Molecule—The smallest unit that a compound may be divided into and still retain its physical and chemical characteristics.

Molybdenum (Mo)—An essential element classified as a micronutrient which is a component of two enzyme systems that are involved in the conversion of nitrate to ammonium (see Chapter 3).

Nitrate—An anion of one atom of nitrogen and three of oxygen to form NO_3^-, which is a common form of N found in soils and that can be readily absorbed by plant roots in order to satisfy the N requirement of a plant.

Nitrite—An anion of one atom of nitrogen and two of oxygen to form NO_2^-, a reduced form of N that exists mostly under anaerobic conditions and is a form of N that is highly toxic to plants.

Nitrogen (N)—An essential element classified as a major element which is a component of amino acids and proteins. Nitrogen exists in the atmosphere as a gas, and in the plant and soil solution as either the nitrate anion or the ammonium cation (see Chapter 2).

Nitrogen Fixing Bacteria—Any of several genera of bacteria that have the ability to convert atmospheric nitrogen into ammonium and nitrate, which can then be used by other organisms.

Nutrient—In plant nutrition use, refers to one of the essential elements and is frequently united to the word element.

Organic Matter—Material that was formed by the bodily processes of an organism and as plant residues. Decaying organic matter (plant and organism residues) can be a source of essential plant nutrients, primarily nitrogen, phosphorus, sulfur, and boron.

Osmosis—The passage of water or another solvent through a membrane in response to differences in the concentrations of dissolved materials on opposite sides of the membrane.

Osmotic Pressure—Force exerted by substances dissolved in water which affects water movement into and out of plant cells. Salts in the soil solution exert some degree of force which can restrict water movement into plant root cells or extract water from them.

Oxygen (O)—An essential element classified as a major element (see Chapter 1).

Passive Absorption—The movement of ions into plant roots carried along with water being absorbed by roots.

Petiole—The stem of a leaf which connects the base of the leaf blade to the stem.

pH—A measure of the acidity or basicity of a liquid, a measure of the number of hydrogen ions present in the liquid (in moles/L), expressed as the negative logarithm. pH ranges from 1 (acid) to 10 (alkaline).

Phloem—The tissue system of a vascular plant through which the sugar and other food substances formed in the leaves are conducted to other parts of the plant. The direction of flow is downward, the driving force being osmotic pressure.

Phosphorus (P)—An essential element classified as a major element which is a component of several enzymes and proteins and an element involved in various energy transfer systems in the plant. Phosphorus exists in the soil solution as an anion in various forms depending on the pH (see Chapter 2).

Photosynthesis—The synthesis of carbohydrates from carbon dioxide and water by living organisms utilizing light energy as an energy source which is catalyzed by chlorophyll according to the following formula: $6CO_2 + 6H_2O + light \rightarrow C_6H_{12}O_6 + 6O_2$.

Plant Analysis—A method of determining the total elemental content of the whole plant or one of its parts, and then relating the concentration found to the well-being of the plant in terms of its elemental requirement (see Chapter 4).

Plant Nutrients—A term used to identify those elements that are essential to plants (see Chapters 2 and 3). Sometimes the term used may be plant nutrient element.

Plant Nutrition—The study of the effects of the essential as well as other elements on the growth and well-being of plants.

Plant Requirement—That quantity of an essential element needed for the normal growth and development of the plant without inducing stress due to its deficiency or excess.

Potassium (K)—An essential element classified as a major element which maintains cellular turgor. Potassium exists in the plant and soil solution as a cation (see Chapter 2).

ppb—An abbreviation for parts per billion, which is 1/1000 of a part per million, expressed in metric units as micrograms per kilogram (µg/kg) in weight units and micrograms per liter (µg/L) in liquid units.

ppm—An abbreviation for parts per million, expressed in metric units as milligrams per kilogram (mg/kg) in weight units and milligrams per liter (mg/L) in liquid units.

Respiration—The set of processes through which energy is obtained from sugars and other carbohydrates in the body of a living organism.

Scorch—Burned leaf margins, a visual symptom typical of potassium deficiency or boron and chloride excess.

Soil Solution—The liquid, water phase of the soil which contains solutes.

Standard Value—The mean concentration of an element in plant tissue based on the analysis results from a large population of normal growing plants.

Sufficiency and Sufficiency Range—The adequate supply of an essential element to the plant. Also, an adequate concentration of an essential element in the plant to satisfy the plant's physiological requirement. The plant in such a condition will look normal in appearance, be healthy and capable of high production.

Sulfur (S)—An essential element classified as a major element which is a component of some proteins and is a component of glucosides that are the source for the characteristic odors of some plants. Sulfur exists in the plant and soil solution as the sulfate anion (see Chapter 2).

Symbiotic Bacteria—Relates to bacteria that infect plant roots of legumes forming nodules on the roots, fixing atmospheric nitrogen, thereby providing N for the plant and obtaining their carbohydrates from the plant.

Tissue Testing—A method for determining the concentration of the soluble form of an element in the plant by analyzing sap that has been physically extracted from a particular plant part, usually from stems or petioles. Tests are usually limited to the determination of nitrate, phosphate, potassium, and iron (see Chapter 5).

Toxicity—The ability of a substance or element to disrupt the normal functions of a plant.

Trace Elements—An obsolete term which was used to identify the micronutrients but today is used to identify those nonessential elements found in plant tissue in very low concentrations.

Tracking—A technique of following through time the essential element content of the rooting media or plant by a sequence of analyses made at specified stages of plant growth.

Water—Dihydrogen oxide. Among the most familiar and ubiquitous of all chemicals, water is also among the most unusual, with a group of unique properties that place it a class by itself. Water is highly polar, can exist is all three phases of matter–liquid, solid, and gaseous, has an extremely high surface tension, and is an excellent solvent.

Xylem—The tissue of a vascular plant through which water and minerals are transported upward from roots to the leaves.

Zinc (Zn)—An essential element classified as a micronutrient which is involved in several enzymatic functions in plants. Zinc exists in the plant and the soil solution as a cation (see Chapter 3).

APPENDIX D

Elemental Requirements by Crop

Elements

The elemental requirements for the major elements, nitrogen (N), phosphorus (P), potassium (K), calcium (Ca), magnesium (Mg), and sulfur (S), and the micronutrients, boron (B), copper (Cu), iron (Fe), manganese (Mn), and zinc (Zn), are given in the following tables.

Crop Categories

One hundred and forty-three crops are grouped into seven crop categories:

1. Agronomic
2. Forage and grasses
3. Fruits and nuts
4. Ornamentals and flowers
5. Tropical plantation crops

6. Turf
7. Vegetables

Elemental Requirement Levels

The elemental requirements are divided into five categories:

1. Very high (VH)
2. High (H)
3. Medium (M)
4. Low (L)
5. Very low (VL)

Those requirements given in parentheses ( ) designate levels not clearly known and therefore assumed.

For that element where neither crop removal and/or growth response to that element is known, a medium (M) requirement is assumed, the only exception being for the element boron where low (L) requirement is always assumed in such cases.

Requirement level

Common name	Scientific name	Major elements							Micronutrients			
		N	P	K	Ca	Mg	S	B	Cu	Fe	Mn	Zn
AGRONOMIC CROPS												
Barley	Hordeum vulgare	M	L	L	L	L	L	L	M	(M)	M	H
Cassava	Manihot esculenta	L	L	H	L	L	M	M	L	M	M	H
Corn, grain	Zea mays	H	M	M	M	M	M	L	(M)	H	(M)	(M)
Oat	Avena sativa	L	L	L	L	L	L	L	M	M	H	M
Peanut	Arachis hypogaea	M	L	L	H	M	M	L	H	M	M	M
Rice	Oryza sativa	L	L	L	L	VL	L	L	L	M	H	M
Rye	Secale cereale	L	VL	VL	(M)	(M)	M	(L)	(M)	M	L	L
Sorghum	Sorghum bicolor	H	M	M	M	L	M	L	L	H	M	H
Soybean	Glycine max	VH	M	M	L	M	H	M	L	M	M	H
Sugar beet	Beta vulgaris	H	L	VH	(M)	H	H	M	L	L	H	L
Sugarcane	Saccharum officinarum	M	M	H	M	M	M	L	M	M	L	M
Tobacco, burley	Nicotiana tabacum	H	VL	M	L	L	L	L	M	M	H	H
Tobacco, flue cured	Nicotiana tabacum	L	VL	M	H	VL	L	L	M	M	H	H
Wheat	Triticum aestivum	L	L	L	L	L	L	L	M	L	M	L
FLOWERS AND ORNAMENTALS												
Fern, leatherleaf	Rumohra adiantiformis	H	M	H	L	VL	M	L	L	L	L	M
Ficus (weeping fig)	Ficus benjamina	H	H	H	L	M	L	H	(M)	L	M	M
Ficus, Decora	Ficus elastica "Decora"	H	L	M	VL	M	L	M	(M)	L	M	M
Ficus (wideleaf rubber)	Ficus elastica	H	H	H	VL	M	(M)	M	(M)	H	M	M
Ficus Fiddleleaf	Ficus lyrata (pandurata)	H	H	H	L	M	M	L	(M)	M	M	M
Ficus (Indian laurel)	Ficus perforata	M	M	M	M	(M)	L	M	(M)	M	M	M
Geranium	Pelargonium x hortorum	H	M	H	L	M	H	L	L	L	L	L
Gerbera (Transvaal daisy)	Gerbera jamesonii	M	M	H	L	L	M	L	M	H	H	M

FLOWERS AND ORNAMENTALS (continued)

Common name	Scientific name	Major elements						Micronutrients				
		N	P	K	Ca	Mg	S	B	Cu	Fe	Mn	Zn
Pothos	Epipremum (Scindapsus) aureum	M	M	H	M	M	(M)	L	M	M	M	M
Rhododendron	Rhododendron spp.	M	M	M	L	M	(M)	L	M	H	M	M
Rose	Rosa odorata	M	M	M	M	M	M	M	M	H	M	M
Sansevieria	Sansevieria trifasciata	L	VL	M	M	(M)	L	L	M	L	L	L
Schefflera	Brassaia actinophylla	H	M	M	M	M	(M)	M	M	M	M	M
Spathiphyllum	Spathiphyllum spp.	M	M	M	M	H	(M)	M	M	H	M	M
Statice	Sticia limonium spp.	H	M	H	L	M	M	L	M	H	M	H
Viburnum	Viburnum suspensum	L	VL	VL	M	L	(M)	L	M	H	M	M
Yucca	Yucca elephantipes	M	M	M	L	L	M	M	L	L	L	L
Gardenia	Gardenia jasminoides	M	L	M	L	L	M	L	L	H	M	M
Gladiolus	Gladiolus x hortulanus	M	H	H	H	M	M	H	M	M	L	L
Gypsophila (Baby's breath)	Gypsophila paniculata	H	M	M	L	M	M	M	(M)	H	M	M
Hydrangea, pink	Hydrangea macrophylla	H	H	H	H	M	L	M	M	H	M	L
Hydrangea, blue	Hydrangea macrophylla	L	L	H	L	M	L	M	M	L	L	L
Daylily	Hemerocallis spp.	M	M	M	M	M	M	M	M	M	M	M
Lily, Easter	Lilium longiflorum	M	L	M	M	M	M	L	M	M	M	M
Palm, areca	Chrysalidocarpus lutescens	M	M	M	L	(M)	(M)	L	M	M	H	M
Palm, chamaedorea	Chamaedorea spp.	M	L	L	L	M	(M)	L	M	M	H	M
Palm, Roebelin	Phoenix roebelenii	M	L	L	L	M	(M)	L	M	M	M	M
Palm, raffia	Raphia farinifera	L	L	M	M	L	(M)	L	L	H	H	M
Peperomia	Peperomia obtusifolia	M	M	M	M	M	M	L	M	L	M	M
Philodendron (Cordatum)	Philodendron scandens	M	M	M	M	M	(M)	L	M	M	M	M
Philodendron, spade-leaf	Philodendron hastatum	L	M	M	M	L	M	L	M	M	M	M

Common Name	Scientific Name													
Philodendron, panda	Philodendron panduriforme	M	M	M	M	L	M	M	M	L	M	M	M	M
Philodendron, split-leaf	Philodendron, Monstera deliciosa	M	(M)	M	M	H	M	M	M	L	L	M	M	M
Philodendron, selloum	Philodendron selloum	H	M	M	M	H	M	M	M	L	M	M	M	M
Pittosporum	Pittosporum tobira	VL	M	M	M	VL	L	L	M	L	M	M	L	M
Podocarpus	Podocarpus macrophyllus var. Maki	L	M	M	VL	L	L	L	M	M	L	L	L	M
Poinsettia	Euphorbia pulcherrima	H	M	M	H	L	H	M	H	M	M	H	M	M
Aglaonema	Aglaomena commutatum	M	L	M	M	M	(M)	(M)	L	(M)	M	(M)	M	(M)
Aster	Callistephus chinensis	M	M	M	M	M	M	(M)	M	(M)	(M)	M	(M)	(M)
Azalea	Rhododendron spp.	M	M	M	(M)	M	M	M	M	M	M	M	M	M
Camellia	Camellia japonica	M	M	M	M	M	M	(M)	M	M	M	M	M	(M)
Carnation	Dianthus caryophyllus	M	M	M	M	M	M	M	M	M	M	M	M	M
Chrysanthemum	Chrysanthemum spp.	H	L	H	H	H	M	M	H	M	M	M	L	M
Dogwood	Cornus spp.	L	L	L	L	L	L	L	L	L	L	L	H	M
Dracena, Warneckii	Dracaena deremensis "Warneckii"	M	L	M	M	M	(M)	(M)	L	M	L	M	M	(M)
Dracena Janet Craig	Dracaena deremensis "Janet Craig"	M	L	M	M	M	(M)	(M)	L	M	L	M	M	(M)
Corn plant	Dracaena fragrans	M	L	M	M	M	(M)	(M)	L	M	L	M	M	(M)
Dracaena marginata	Dracaena marginata	H	L	H	H	H	(M)	H	L	L	L	H	M	(M)
Fern, Boston	Nephrolepsis exaltata "Bostoniensis"	M	L	M	M	L	L	(M)	M	(M)	M	L	M	M

FORAGES AND GRASSES

Common Name	Scientific Name													
Alfalfa	Medicago sativa	VH	M	H	M	M	H	H	H	M	M	M	M	M
Coastal Bermuda	Cynodon dactylon	VH	H	M	H	M	M	H	H	H	M	M	M	M
Bromegrass	Bromus inermis	M	M	(M)	M	(M)	VL	L	L	M	(M)	M	M	(M)
Clover	Trifolium spp.	H	H	M	M	M	M	M	M	M	M	M	H	H
Corn, silage	Zea mays	H	M	M	M	M	M	M	M	M	H	H	H	H
Fescue, tall	Festuca elatior	M	L	(M)	(M)	(H)	H	H	VL	L	L	M	M	(M)
Guinea grass	Panicum maximum	H	M	M	(M)	(M)	H	H	H	M	M	M	M	(M)
Napier grass	Pennisetum purpureum	H	M	M	(M)	(M)	H	(M)	H	(M)	H	H	M	(M)
Orchard grass	Dactylis glomerata	H	H	H	M	(M)	H	H	H	L	H	M	H	H
Pangola grass	Digitaria decumbens	H	M	M	M	(M)	H	H	H	H	L	M	M	(M)
Paragrass	Brachiaria spp.	H	M	M	L	(M)	H	H	H	L	L	M	H	(M)

Common name	Scientific name	Major elements						Micronutrients				
		N	P	K	Ca	Mg	S	B	Cu	Fe	Mn	Zn
FORAGES AND GRASSES (continued)												
Pensacola bahia	*Paspalum notatum* var. *saurae*	H	L	L	L	M	M	M	M	M	H	H
Ryegrass	*Lolium* spp.	M	M	M	(M)	L	M	M	L	L	M	M
Sorghum , forage	*Sorghum bicolor*	H	H	H	(M)	M	(M)	(M)	(M)	H	M	H
Sorghum, Sudan	*Sorghum sudanese*	H	H	H	(M)	M	M	(M)	(M)	H	M	H
Timothy	*Plebum pratense*	M	L	M	M	L	L	L	L	(M)	M	M
FRUITS AND NUTS												
Apple	*Malus* spp.	L	L	M	M	L	L	H	M	M	H	H
Apricot	*Prunus armeniaca*	L	VL	L	L	M	L	M	M	H	M	M
Avocado	*Persea americana*	L	L	L	M	L	L	M	M	M	H	M
Banana	*Musa* spp.	VH	VH	VH	L	H	M	H	L	L	L	L
Blackberry	*Rubus* spp.	L	L	L	L	M	L	L	M	M	M	L
Cherry, sour	*Prunus cerasus*	M	VL	M	M	L	L	M	(M)	M	M	M
Coconut	*Cocos nucifera*	M	L	M	M	L	L	M	(M)	H	H	H
Grape	*Vitis* spp.	L	L	L	L	VL	M	H	M	H	H	H
Grapefruit	*Cirtus x paradisi*	M	L	M	M	M	M	M	M	M	M	M
Lemon	*Cirtus limon*	H	L	H	H	M	M	H	(M)	H	H	H
Lime, Persian	*Citrus aurantifolia,* "Tahiti"	H	M	M	M	M	(M)	M	L	M	M	M
Mango	*Mangifera indica*	H	L	L	H	L	L	L	H	H	H	H
Orange	*Citrus sinensis*	VH	M	M	M	M	M	M	M	M	M	M
Papaya	*Carica papaya*	VH	L	M	M	H	L	L	M	H	M	M
Peach	*Prunus persica*	L	L	M	L	L	L	L	M	M	M	H
Pear	*Pyrus communis*	L	VL	VL	L	L	L	M	M	L	M	H
Pecan	*Carya illinoensis*	M	M	L	M	M	L	L	M	L	M	H

Common name	Scientific name													
Pineapple	*Ananas comosus*	M	L	M	M	L	M	L	L	M	L	H	L	M
Raspberry	*Rubus idaeus*	L	H	L	L	H	(M)	M	L	M	M	H	H	L
Strawberry	*Fragaria chiloensis*	M	L	M	M	M	L	M	L	L	M	M	L	M
TROPICAL PLANTATION CROPS														
Cacao	*Theobroma cacao*	(M)	(M)	H	VH	M	(M)	H	(M)	L	(M)	(M)	(M)	(M)
Coffee	*Coffea arabica*	L	L	L	M	M	M	M	M	M	M	H	L	L
Coffee	*Coffea canaphora*	L	L	L	H	M	M	M	M	L	M	H	L	L
Oil palm	*Elaeis guineensis*	(M)	(M)	M	M	L	L	L	(M)	L	(M)	(M)	(M)	(M)
TURF														
Bahia grass	*Paspalum notatum*	(M)	M	L	M	M	L	L	L	L	L	M	M	(M)
Bent grass	*Agrostis* spp.	(M)	M	M	M	M	L	L	L	L	L	M	(M)	(M)
Bermuda grass	*Cynodon dactylon*	(M)	H	VH	M	H	L	L	L	L	L	M	M	(M)
Centipede	*Eremochloa ophiuroides*	M	L	VL	L	L	L	L	L	L	L	H	H	M
Fescue, red	*Festuca rubra*	M	M	M	M	L	L	L	L	M	L	L	L	M
Kentucky bluegrass	*Poa pratensis*	(M)	M	M	M	L	L	L	L	M	L	H	H	(M)
Ryegrass	*Lolium* spp.	(M)	H	H	M	M	M	(M)	L	M	L	M	M	(M)
St. Augustine	*Stenotaphrum secundatum*	(M)	M	M	M	L	L	M	L	L	L	M	(M)	(M)
Zoysia	*Zoysia matrella*	(M)	M	M	M	M	M	M	L	L	L	M	(M)	(M)
VEGETABLES														
Asparagus	*Asparagus officinalis*	L	L	M	M	H	H	H	M	H	M	M	(M)	L
Bean lima	*Phaseolus* spp.	H	(M)	VL	VL	L	(M)	L	(M)	L	(M)	M	(M)	H
Bean, snap	*Phaseolus vulgaris*	H	M	L	M	M	(M)	M	(M)	L	L	M	M	H
Beet, table	*Beta vulgaris*	(M)	H	VH	VH	H	M	H	H	H	H	(M)	(M)	(M)
Broccoli	*Brassica oleracea, Botrytis Group*	(M)	H	H	M	H	M	H	H	H	M	(M)	M	(M)
Brussels sprouts	*Brassica oleracea, Gemmifer Group*	M	H	M	M	H	L	H	H	H	M	(M)	M	M
Cabbage	*Brassica oleracea, Capitata Group*	M	L	VL	VL	M	L	M	L	L	L	L	(M)	M
Canteloupe	*Cucumis melo, Reticulatus Group*	(M)	M	L	M	M	M	L	H	H	(M)	(M)	(M)	(M)
Carrot	*Daucus carota*	(M)	L	VH	VH	H	M	M	H	H	M	H	L	(M)
Celery	*Apium graveolens*	M	VH	H	VH	VH	M	M	H	H	M	M	M	M

Common name	Scientific name	Requirement level										
		Major elements						Micronutrients				
		N	P	K	Ca	Mg	S	B	Cu	Fe	Mn	Zn
VEGETABLES (continued)												
Corn, sweet	Zea mays var. rugosa	M	L	M	L	L	L	L	L	M	H	M
Cucumber	Cucumis sativus	M	VL	H	M	L	L	M	L	L	M	M
Eggplant	Solanum melongena	M	M	M	M	M	M	M	M	H	H	M
Endive	Cichorium endiva	L	L	M	M	M	L	M	M	(M)	H	M
Kale	Brassica oleracea, Acephala Group	H	M	M	M	M	M	M	M	L	H	M
Lettuce	Lactuca sativa	M	L	M	L	L	L	L	L	H	H	M
Okra	Abelmoschus esculentus	VL	L	L	L	L	H	M	H	(M)	(M)	(M)
Onion	Allium, Cepa Group	M	M	M	(M)	L	L	L	L	(M)	H	M
Pea, English	Pisum sativum	M	VL	M	H	VL	L	M	M	L	H	M
Pepper, bell	Capsicum annuum, Grossum Group	M	M	M	(M)	M	(M)	M	L	M	H	L
Potato, Irish	Solanum tuberosum	H	H	H	M	M	M	L	L	L	H	M
Potato, sweet	Ipomoea batatas	L	L	M	L	L	L	M	M	(M)	M	(M)
Radish	Raphanus sativus	L	L	M	M	M	M	M	M	H	H	M
Rhubarb	Rheum rhaponticum	H	M	H	M	M	(M)	L	(M)	(M)	(M)	(M)
Spinach	Spinacia oleracea	M	L	L	H	M	M	M	M	M	(M)	M
Squash	Cucurbita pepo	L	VL	L	M	L	L	L	L	H	H	M
Tomato	Lycopersicon esculentum	H	M	H	M	M	M	M	M	H	H	H
Turnip	Brassica rapa, Rapifera gr.	M	L	M	(M)	(M)	H	H	M	(M)	M	(M)
Watermelon	Citrullus lanatus	M	M	M	H	H	(M)	M	H	(M)	(M)	(M)

APPENDIX E

Nitrogen, Phosphorus, Potassium, Magnesium, and Sulfur Content of Crops

Crop	Yield	Pounds per acre (lbs/A)				
		N	P_2O_5	K_2O	Mg	S
AGRONOMIC CROPS						
Corn	Grain, 9.5 t/ha	129	71	47	10	12
	Stover	62	18	188	30	9
Flax	30 bu	76	20	16	7	4
	2100 lb straw	19	5	44	6	5
Grain sorghum	8000 lb grain	120	60	30	14	22
	8000 lb stover	130	30	170	30	16
Peanut[a]	4000 lb nuts	140	22	35	5	10
	5000 lb vines	100	17	150	20	11

| | | Pounds per acre (lbs/A) | | | | |
Crop	Yield	N	P_2O_5	K_2O	Mg	S
AGRONOMIC CROPS (continued)						
Rice	7000 lb grain	77	46	28	8	5
	7000 lb straw	35	14	140	6	7
Soybean[a]	60 bu	252	49	87	17	12
	7000 lb stalks, leaves, pods	84	16	58	10	13
Sugar beet	307 roots	125	15	250	27	10
	16 T tops	130	25	300	53	35
Sugarcane	100 T stalks	160	90	335	40	54
	tops and trash	200	66	275	60	32
Tobacco	3000 lb leaf	85	15	155	15	12
(flue-cured)	3600 lb stalks, tops, suckers	41	11	102	9	7
Tobacco (burley)	4000 lb leaf	145	14	150	18	24
	3600 lb stalks, tops, suckers	95	16	114	9	21
FRUIT CROPS						
Apple	600 boxes (42 lb)	20	8	50	2	b
	blossom, fruit, new wood	80	38	130	22	b
Coconut	3600 nuts +12 fronds lost annually	75	25	120	20	12
Grape	12 T fruit	66	23	120	b	b
	vines	36	12	36	b	b
Orange	600 boxes (90 lb)	90	23	162	10	7
	trees (70/A)	175	32	168	28	21
Peach	600 bu	35	10	65	b	b
	tree annually	60	30	55	b	b
VEGETABLE CROPS						
Cabbage	35 T	b	35	128	9	64
	23 T stem and leaf	b	28	121	27	b
Celery	75 T tops	255	130	660	b	b
	roots	25	35	70	b	b
Cucumber	10 T	40	14	66	4	b
	vines	50	14	108	21	b
Onion	30 T	180	80	160	18	37
Pea	3 T	45	9	17	8	b
	pods and vines	105	17	62	14	b
Potato	500 cwt	150	80	264	12	12
	vines	102	34	90	20	12

Crop	Yield	Pounds per acre (lbs/A)				
		N	P_2O_5	K_2O	Mg	S
VEGETABLE CROPS (continued)						
Sweet potato	400 bu	53	26	126	5	b
	vines	50	14	84	6	b
Snap bean	4 T	70	21	77	8	b
	plants	66	12	86	9	b
Table beet	25 T roots	170	30	210	30	13
	20 T tops	190	13	370	74	28
Tomato	40 T fruit	144	67	288	10	28
	4400 lb vines	88	20	175	26	26
GRASSES AND LEGUMES						
Guineagrass	11.5 T	288	101	436	99	46
Johnsongrass	12 T	890	190	630	60	50
Lespedezaa	3 T	150	50	150	25	20
Napiergrass	12.5 T	303	147	605	63	75
Paragrass	12 T	300	98	460	79	41
Tall fescue	3 T	135	65	185	13	b

[a] Legumes can get most of their nitrogen from the air.
[b] Figures unavailable.

Source: Potash and Phosphate Institute.

APPENDIX F

Nitrogen, Phosphorus, Potassium, Magnesium, and Sulfur Utilization by Crops

		Pounds per acre (lbs/A)				
Crop	Yield	N	P_2O_5	K_2O	Mg	S
AGRONOMIC						
Barley	100 bu	150	55	150	17	20
Corn	180 bu	240	100	240	50	30
Corn silage	32 tons	240	100	300	50	30
Cotton	1500 lbs lint	180	63	162	24	20
Grain sorghum	8000 lbs	250	90	200	44	38
Oats	100 bu	115	40	145	20	20
Peanut (nuts)	4000 lbs	240	39	185	25	21
Rice	7000 lbs	112	60	168	14	12

Crop	Yield	Pounds per acre (lbs/A)				
		N	P_2O_5	K_2O	Mg	S
AGRONOMIC (continued)						
Soybean	60 bu	336	65	145	27	25
Sugar beet	30 tons	255	40	550	80	45
Sugar cane	100 tons	360	156	610	100	86
Tobacco (flue-cured)	3000 lbs	126	26	257	24	19
Tobacco (burley)	4000 lbs	240	30	264	27	45
Wheat	80 bu	186	54	162	24	20
FRUITS						
Apple	600 boxes	100	46	180	24	—
Banana	1200 plants	400	400	1500	156	—
Grapes	12 tons	102	35	156	—	—
Oranges	600 boxes	265	55	330	38	28
Peach	600 bu	95	40	120	—	—
Pineapple	35,700 lbs	153	125	596	64	14
VEGETABLES						
Cabbage	35 tons	228	63	249	36	64
Celery	75 tons	280	165	750	—	—
Irish potato	500 cwt	252	114	354	32	24
Lettuce	20 tons	100	44	198	7	—
Snap bean	4 tons	138	32	163	17	—
Sweet potato	400 bu	103	40	210	11	—
Table beet	25 tons	360	43	580	104	41
Tomato	40 tons	232	87	463	36	54
GRASSES AND LEGUMES						
Alfalfa	8 tons	450	80	480	40	40
Clover grass	6 tons	300	90	360	30	30
Coastal Bermuda	10 tons	500	140	420	45	45
Orchard grass	6 tons	300	100	375	25	35
Timothy	4 tons	150	55	250	10	16
Bermuda grass	4 tons	225	40	160	20	15
Bromegrass	5 tons	166	66	254	10	20
Sorghum sudan	7.5 tons	319	122	467	47	—
Bentgrass	2.5 tons	225	80	160	12	10
Pangola grass	11.8 tons	229	108	430	67	46
PLANTATION CROPS						
Coconut	3600 nuts	75	25	120	20	12
Oil palm	33,882 lbs	615	316	481	196	—

Source: Potash and Phosphate Institute

INDEX